FOURIER SERIES

Also by N. W. Gowar

MATHEMATICS FOR TECHNOLOGY:
A NEW APPROACH
with M. Bruckheimer and R. E. Scraton)

*

Also in this Series

ORDINARY DIFFERENTIAL EQUATIONS
M. R. Scott and B. A. L. Hart

VECTOR ANALYSIS
Sheila Brenner

MATHEMATICS FOR SCIENCE AND
TECHNOLOGY
Editor: EDWIN KERR

FOURIER SERIES

N. W. GOWAR, M.Phil., F.I.M.A.

J. E. BAKER, B.Sc.

1974

Distributed in the United States by
CRANE, RUSSAK & COMPANY, INC.
347 Madison Avenue
New York, New York 10017

Published by
Chatto & Windus Ltd
42 William IV Street, London W.C.2
with
William Collins Sons and Co. Ltd
144 Cathedral Street
Glasgow C.2

ISBN 0 00 460910 7 (hardback)
ISBN 0 00 460907 7 (paperback)

Printed in Great Britain
at the University Printing House, Cambridge
(Brooke Crutchley, University Printer)

Contents

Foreword

by

EDWIN KERR

Chief Officer, Council for National Academic Awards

In a rapidly changing technological society, the practising engineer or scientist can never regard his technical knowledge as complete, and so his main asset is an ability to understand new material and to recognise it in familiar terms. This makes irrelevant the idea of a 'mathematical toolkit'. In its place, there has to be a framework from which any required skill can be quickly assimilated.

This series of mathematics books has been specially written for 2nd and 3rd year students of technology and science, the material being presented rigorously and in the modern idiom. Each volume stands independently but is linked in style and treatment with the other titles in the series. The writers have two aims in view: first, to make already familiar mathematical processes more understandable and acceptable to the non-specialist: second, to provide a motivation for the many mathematical techniques which are increasingly required by the technologist. The result has been to give a change of emphasis to the traditional treatment, so that each technical topic is related to the body of mathematics to which it properly belongs, so as to direct students to look at the underlying structure of a problem and how a particular technique is related to a more general mathematical concept. This does not mean that technical facility is entirely ignored, but that it is treated as a subsidiary objective. Wherever appropriate, analytical and computational approaches to a subject are considered together.

The underlying purpose of the whole series is to give the enquiring student practical help towards an understanding of his problems, in terms of current mathematical thought.

Preface

The subject of Fourier Series occupies a place in the mathematics curriculum of almost every engineering syllabus. One common approach in such courses is to teach the technique of *finding the Fourier Series* of a collection of tried and tested functions. It is not so common to find the topic given its engineering significance, and even less common to find it set in its appropriate mathematical context. The purpose of this book is to do the latter and at the same time to explain the technique of finding Fourier Series. We have not attempted seriously to discuss the engineering applications, for these differ so much according to the area of application and, more important, the authors are not engineers.

It is our firm belief, however, that an appreciation of the relevance of any mathematical topic is greatly enhanced when its mathematical background is understood. Such a background is usually suggestive of a number of related topics and, consequently, related applications. Furthermore, it is one of the ways in which a student can gain confidence in mathematics. To learn a succession of isolated techniques may be convenient and easy at the time, but such a policy is short-sighted and can only create the uneasy feeling of one who is given a few pieces from a jigsaw and never allowed a sight of the picture on the box. An engineer with a sense of the power and ubiquity of mathematical ideas has every chance of solving problems with imagination and inventiveness. He will also be in the happy position of being able to communicate with mathematicians and update his mathematics throughout his career.

There seem to be two ways of approaching Fourier Series: via their use in approximating functions and their use in analysing functions. We have adopted the former approach, for it leads most easily to a discussion of the vector space and Euclidean space background to the subject that we wish to emphasize. The latter approach leads to Fourier transforms and integral transforms in general; this is to be subject of another book in this series. Throughout the book, we tend to move from the general to the particular and back again; but, on the whole, the particular is nearly always the special case of trigonometric Fourier series. This is intentional for this particular type of orthogonal expansion is the main topic of the book, and it is hoped that this topic will give the reader a base line from which he can launch off into more general considerations and other examples.

In Chapter 1 we are interested in seeing just how it might be possible to approximate to a function using a series of sine and cosine functions. In Chapter 2 we develop the technique which is used to calculate the coefficients in such a series. Chapter 3 is essentially a collection of examples and exercises on the calculation of particular Fourier Series.

Having seen how to calculate Fourier Series, the next step is to investigate the manner in which such a series converges, and the conditions under which it does so. This is the object of Chapter 4. Chapter 5 consists of a series of quite lengthy examples of problems which require Fourier Series for their solution. It is intended that the reader follow a selection of these which appeal to his particular taste – it is by no means essential to the development of the text that he reads them all. The book concludes, in Chapter 6, with an indication of some of the general theory of orthogonal expansions. Throughout the text, there are a number of exercises. There are not many, but they are intended to form part of the text. The reader is therefore encouraged to attempt all of them – they are all supplied with fully worked solutions at the back of the book. These exercises are not sufficient to give the student the confidence that comes from trying to tackle problems on his own. Opportunities for such efforts are provided by a collection of exercises at the end of the book, for which answers are also given.

We would both like to record our appreciation to Maxim Bruckheimer for his profuse and constructive comments on the typescript. We have taken appropriate remedial action in most cases, and we obviously take full responsibility for rejecting those suggestions which, it may transpire, we should not have done.

N.W.G.
J.E.B.

Note

We have assumed that the reader is familiar with the mathematics covered in:

M. Bruckheimer, N. W. Gowar and R. E. Scraton
  Mathematics for Technology: A New Approach. (Chatto and Windus.)

We make a number of references to this book which are indicated by

(see M.T.)

as, for example, on page 1 opposite.

We have also used, as far as possible, the mathematical notation in M.T. However a number of symbols occur frequently enough in this book to warrant special mention.

f   a function, when we wish to emphasise that it belongs to a vector space, as opposed to

$f(x)$ its image value

Thus, for example, we write

cos m, **sin n**   to denote the trignometric functions which have image values

cos mx, sin nx respectively.

1 · Approximation

*The use of Fourier Series in Mathematics and in applications is
widespread and arises predominantly in situations involving a function
which is periodic or defined over a finite interval of the real numbers.
Periodic functions frequently arise in problems involving vibrations;
sometimes pleasant, as with a musical note, sometimes not so pleasant,
as with a pneumatic drill outside the front door. Functions such as these
can be represented by Fourier Series. Such series can be used both to
analyse functions and to approximate them.*

This chapter outlines a situation in which the idea of approximation
is important in mathematics and also some of the difficulties that
arise when the term 'approximation' is being used. The remarks are
illustrated by two types of approximation, polynomial approximation
and trigonometric approximation. These are used because the reader
has probably met one type of polynomial approximation already –
notably those obtained by using finite parts of Maclaurin or Taylor
series (see M.T.) – and one type of trigonometric approximation –
Fourier Series – is the main subject of this book.

Fourier Series are used for approximating a given function by a
series consisting of sine and cosine functions. The series

$$\cos x - \sin x - \frac{\cos 2x}{4} + \frac{\sin 2x}{2} - \frac{\cos 3x}{9} + \frac{\sin 3x}{3} - \ldots$$

is an example of a Fourier Series. They are also used to approximate
the solutions of differential equations, because that is often the best
way of solving certain types of equation. They could also be used to
approximate functions which are not fully and explicitly specified, as
might arise with tabulated results from an experiment. To explain
this point a little more fully let us look, for a moment, at what is
involved in an experiment.

In its simplest terms, an experiment can be regarded as a process
in which a set of inputs is fed into a device of some sort and the
corresponding outputs recorded.

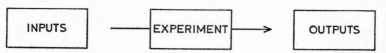

The purpose of the experiment is to infer, from the limited data available, the way the device would handle a new input which has not yet been tried. To do this, the idea is to set up a mathematical model, whereby the behaviour of the device is described by a function and the set of all possible inputs and outputs form respectively the domain and the range of the function.

For example, suppose an experiment gave rise to the following set of pairs.

Input	Output
0	0
1	1.5
2	1
3	1.75
4	3.5

On a graph, this would give the following picture.

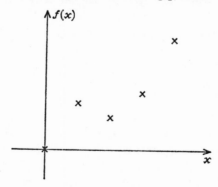

The experiment itself does not tell us what the output would be for an input 1.4, 2.3 or any other non-tabulated value, and the art of the experimenter is to try to use the available information to take a reasoned guess at what such an output would be. One way of doing this would be to draw a curve through these points and to assume that this curve is the graph of a function which gives a reasonable approximation to the behaviour of the device.

A first guess might be a straight line.

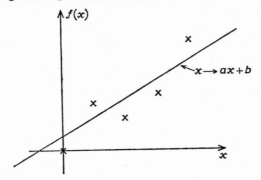

This is rather crude; perhaps a parabola might be better,

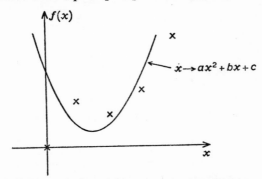

or a cubic, which takes account of the ups *and* downs,

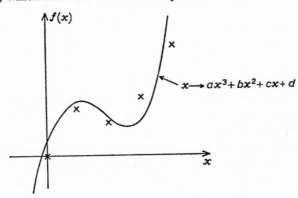

3

or perhaps a graph like this,

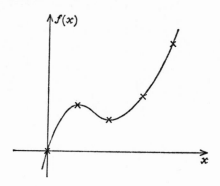

or this.

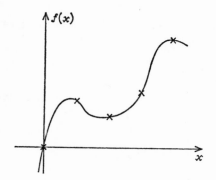

These curves are the graphs of functions built up by adding together appropriate multiples of the polynomial functions

$$x \to x$$
$$x \to x^2$$
$$\vdots$$
$$x \to x^n$$
$$\vdots$$

all with domain R, the set of real numbers, or some subset of R. These simple functions can be considered as the building blocks for the approximation. Mathematically, we are saying that if f is the function which describes the behaviour of the device, then one way of trying to approximate to f is to use the data available to make as good a guess as we can at the numbers $a_0, a_1, ..., a_n$, to make the approximation

$$f(x) \simeq a_0 + a_1 x + a_2 x^2 + ... + a_n x^n$$

as sensible as possible. What we mean by 'sensible' here opens up a whole realm of difficulties and really amounts to how we interpret the symbol $\simeq$. Should the approximating curve pass through the points? Should we sacrifice exact correspondence with the data for smoothness of the curve? How much faith can we put in the data?... and so on. We do not intend to go into those difficulties now. Rather, we would like to pick up a different point.

The polynomial functions are fairly obvious choices for this work – they are just about the simplest functions to choose. But that is not to say they are the best. In fact, as we shall be seeing later there are all sorts of functions which are useful as 'building blocks' for approximations. The type of function to use depends on the circumstances. One may be concerned with fast, accurate computation, or there may be some other factor influencing the choice of component functions. For example, suppose the device in question were a hi-fi system. If the system is to be good, then it will need to reproduce as well as possible any one of a whole range of sounds. Clearly it is not feasible to test every possible sound as an input. But a sample of inputs could be tested, and then one would be interested in inferring from this experiment what the equipment would do for other inputs. So once again we are back in the situation where from a certain amount of available information, one wishes to construct an approximation to a function which describes a device. But this time extra information is available – the device is intended to deal with sounds which are periodic. This, in turn, means that the graph of a sound wave repeats itself over and over again at a fixed interval, like a sine wave or a cosine wave.

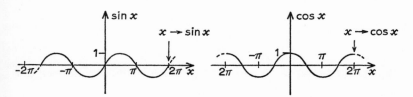

They could have different frequencies,

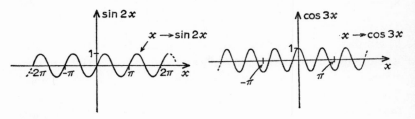

or different amplitudes.

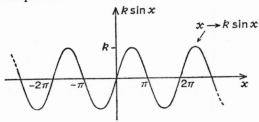

Just as with polynomial approximations, we can form trigonometric approximations by adding together appropriate multiples of trigonometric functions to give

$$f(x) \simeq a_0 + a_1 \cos x + a_2 \cos 2x + \ldots + a_n \cos nx$$
$$+ b_1 \sin x + b_2 \sin 2x + \ldots + b_n \sin nx.$$

The coefficients $a_0, a_1, \ldots, a_n, b_1, \ldots, b_n$ would have to be chosen to make the symbol $\simeq$ meaningful in some sense or other. For example, if we wanted to make the approximating curve pass through known points, determined by the experiment, then the coefficients would be determined from a set of equations such as

$$a_0 + a_1 \cos 0 + b_1 \sin 0 + \ldots = f(0) = 0,$$
$$a_0 + a_1 \cos 1 + b_1 \sin 1 + \ldots = f(1) = 1.5,$$
$$a_0 + a_1 \cos 2 + b_1 \sin 2 + \ldots = f(2) = 1,$$
$$a_0 + a_1 \cos 3 + b_1 \sin 3 + \ldots = f(3) = 1.75,$$
$$a_0 + a_1 \cos 4 + b_1 \sin 4 + \ldots = f(4) = 3.5.$$

This would be the set of equations that one would obtain from the table that we had in the earlier example.

6

In this particular case we have only five equations so we must be prepared to accept an approximation to the function which contains only five terms; there are only enough equations for us to be able to determine five coefficients. We are left then with the problem of solving the above equations to find the unknown coefficients a_0, a_1, b_1, a_2 and b_2.

This can be done using a computer – if you were to try solving the equations by hand, you might grow old in the attempt, miss out on the good things in life and never read further, so don't! The coefficients are

Coefficient	Value
a_0	1.46
a_1	−1.04
b_1	−0.50
a_2	−0.42
b_2	0.94

So we get

$$f(x) \simeq 1.46 - 1.04\cos x - 0.50\sin x - 0.42\cos 2x + 0.94\sin 2x.$$

The graph of this approximation is

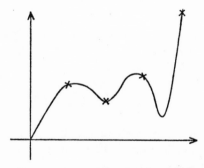

If we had more data – more pairs of input and output values, then, following the line of approach that we used above, we ought to be able to increase the number of terms in the series which we used to approximate the function. But if we increased the number of specified points until they became an interval of the real line, we would have an infinity of equations, each with the possibility of having an infinity of unknowns. Clearly the above method for solving the problem would get out of hand.

7

Whether we are making a *trigonometric* or a *polynomial* approximation to $f(x)$, we can calculate $(n+1)$ coefficients if we know $(n+1)$ points through which the graph of f must pass. As the number of specified points increases, we can take advantage of the new information by taking more terms in the approximation. It is not really clear why this *should* give a better approximation, but intuitively it would seem foolish to ignore information which is available. This is usually the way mathematics works – one lets intuition have its head and if it leads to fruitful answers, then one tries to justify the argument (in a rigorous way) later.

From the point of view of performing an experiment, there is of course a limit to the number of input/output pairs that can be obtained, but this idea does lead us on to another situation where we might want to use an approximation. Sometimes, we have a function which is completely specified throughout its domain, such as

$$f: x \to \frac{1}{1+x} \quad (x \in \{x: 0 \leqslant x < 1\}),$$

but we wish to write it in an alternative form, such as

$$f: x \to 1 - x + x^2 - x^3 + \dots \quad (x \in \{x: 0 \leqslant x < 1\}).$$

If, as in this case, the alternative involves an infinite series, then for all practical situations one can only take a finite number of terms into account and get for example,

$$\frac{1}{1+x} \simeq 1 - x + x^2 - x^3 + x^4 \quad (x \in \{x: 0 \leqslant x < 1\}).$$

Alternatively, we may wish to use trigonometric terms in the approximation. That is to say we may want to calculate $a_0, a_1, \dots, a_n$, $b_1, \dots, b_n$ so that we can write

$$\frac{1}{1+x} \simeq a_0 + a_1 \cos x + b_1 \sin x + \dots + a_n \cos nx + b_n \sin nx$$
$$(x \in \{0 \leqslant x < 1\}).$$

But whatever type of function we use for the approximation, polynomials, trigonometric functions, or anything else we care to dream up, we still need to know how and to what extent we can rely on the symbol $\simeq$. When we were dealing with functions specified only at discrete points in the domain, we were able to take the naive point of view and require that the approximating formula does at least give the 'correct' answers at these points. But now, if we want to 'fit' the approximating function to the given function f throughout the domain then we have to chose the coefficients so that

$$a_0 + a_1 x + a_2 x^2 + \ldots + a_n x^n,$$

or $\qquad a_0 + a_1 \cos x + b_1 \sin x + a_2 \cos 2x + \ldots + b_n \sin nx,$

or whatever approximation we are using, can be made as close as we please to $f(x)$ throughout the domain by making n large enough.

If this is possible, then there are no great problems for in such cases, the above functions can justifiably be said to approximate to the function f for the purpose of calculating images. The difficulty arises when the approximation breaks down at various points in the domain. For example, suppose in the diagrams the light curves repre-

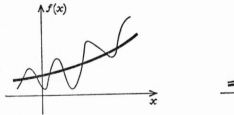
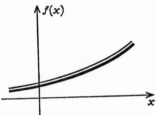

sent two possible approximations to the heavy curve. In the first case, the images coincide at several places; in the second case they coincide nowhere. Yet one would presumably choose the second case as offering a better approximation to the function. There is clearly a different approach required to discuss the convergence of a series of images at a point rather than the convergence of a sequence of functions over their domain. We shall see in later chapters just how these difficulties arise and can be tackled for the trigonometric type of approximations that we have already mentioned. This type of approximation is one of the most important in mathematics both in its immediate application and in the scope of the generalisations that it affords.

When the coefficients a_i and b_i are calculated in the manner which we shall develop in subsequent chapters, the series

$$a_0 + a_1 \cos x + a_2 \cos 2x + \ldots$$
$$+ b_1 \sin x + b_2 \sin 2x + \ldots$$

is called the *Fourier Series* for $f(x)$, after the French mathematician Joseph Fourier, who first used this method to analyse the flow of heat in solids early in the 19th century. The coefficients a_0, a_1, a_2, ..., b_1, b_2, ... are called *Fourier coefficients*; we shall write

$$f(x) \simeq a_0 + a_1 \cos x + a_2 \cos 2x + \ldots$$
$$+ b_1 \sin x + b_2 \sin 2x + \ldots$$

and
$$\mathbf{f} \simeq a_0 \mathbf{1} + a_1 \cos + a_2 \cos 2 + \ldots$$
$$+ b_1 \sin + b_2 \sin 2 + \ldots.$$

The whole process of finding out how closely a Fourier Series approximates to a function is essentially an investigation into how well we can justify the replacement of $\simeq$ by $=$ in these formulae.

We shall see that there is a very wide class of functions which can be approximated very successfully by Fourier Series. It would appear that this class is very restricted because the sine and cosine functions have *period* 2π and so the function

$$x \to a_0 + a_1 \cos x + a_2 \cos 2x + \ldots$$
$$+ b_1 \sin x + b_2 \sin 2x + \ldots$$

will also repeat itself with period 2π.

So if we have a function with domain $\{x : 0 \leqslant x \leqslant 10\}$, for example, we shall be in trouble, because our approximating function will repeat its behaviour in the sub-interval $\{x : 0 \leqslant x \leqslant 2\pi\}$ through the rest of the domain. This difficulty can be overcome by using the functions

$$x \to 1$$
$$x \to \cos \frac{2\pi x}{10}$$
$$x \to \cos \frac{4\pi x}{10}$$
$$\vdots$$
$$x \to \sin \frac{2\pi x}{10}$$
$$x \to \sin \frac{4\pi x}{10}$$
$$\vdots$$

all with domain R. The resulting approximating function will have period 10, and so we can specify how we want it to behave over the required interval.

We shall be seeing in a later chapter how, in general, if we wish to approximate a function with domain an interval of length L, we can use functions of the forms

$$x \to \sin \frac{2\pi mx}{L}$$

and

$$x \to \cos \frac{2\pi mx}{L}.$$

But the function

$$x \to \sin \frac{2\pi mx}{L},$$

for example, is just the composite function

$$(x \to \sin mx) \circ \left(x \to \frac{2\pi x}{L}\right).$$

In other words the essential role is still played by the basic sine and cosine functions, but the x values are first scaled by a factor $\frac{2\pi}{L}$. The calculations are less complicated if this scaling factor does not appear, so we shall deal first with functions specified over a domain length 2π. Further we shall take the particular domain

$$\{x: -\pi \leqslant x \leqslant \pi\}.$$

We shall see later that neither of these simplifications produces any restriction on the type of functions which can be approximated.

One further remark about domains. Suppose the given function has domain $\{x: -\pi \leqslant x \leqslant \pi\}$. Then the function is not defined outside this interval. But the expression

$$a_0 + a_1 \cos x + a_2 \cos 2x + \ldots$$
$$+ b_1 \sin x + b_2 \sin 2x + \ldots$$

makes sense for *any* real value of x and so the approximating function can have as its domain the complete set of real numbers. But still we might be able to say that the specified function and the approximating function are equal over the common part of their domains. Thus, the

11

type of functions that we are thinking about when we are talking about Fourier Series approximations are either functions which are defined on a finite interval, or functions which are periodic.

Exercise 1

Find the period of the following functions:

$$\left.\begin{array}{ll} \text{(i)} & x \to \sin \pi(x-a); \\ \text{(ii)} & x \to \cos^2 x; \\ \text{(iii)} & x \to \sin(x^2); \end{array}\right\} \quad (x \in \mathrm{R}).$$

Summary of Chapter 1

When
$$f(x) \simeq a_0 + a_1 \cos x + a_2 \cos 2x + \ldots$$
$$+ b_1 \sin x + b_2 \sin 2x + \ldots$$

or alternatively
$$\mathbf{f} \simeq a_0 \mathbf{1} + a_1 \cos + a_2 \cos 2 + \ldots$$
$$+ b_1 \sin + b_2 \sin 2 + \ldots$$

the right-hand side is called the *Fourier Series* of **f**. The numbers $a_0, a_1, a_2, \ldots, b_1, b_2, \ldots$ are called the *Fourier coefficients* of **f**.

If a function is defined on an interval of length L, we replace

$$\cos mx \quad \text{by} \quad \cos \left(\frac{m \pi x}{L} \right)$$

and
$$\sin nx \quad \text{by} \quad \sin \left(\frac{n \pi x}{L} \right)$$

in the above expressions.

2 · Fourier coefficients

The problem of finding Fourier coefficients is closely allied to a similar problem in vector algebra. Many ideas which are familiar in vector algebra can be carried over to the new situation of finding Fourier coefficients.

In this chapter, the aim is to take the first step towards devising a procedure for finding an approximation to a given function. We have seen the form that the approximation is going to take; we have to find the coefficients

$$a_0, a_1, b_1, a_2, b_2, \ldots$$

in the formula
$$\mathbf{f} \simeq a_0 \mathbf{1} + a_1 \cos + a_2 \cos 2 + \ldots$$
$$+ b_1 \sin + b_2 \sin 2 + \ldots.$$

A typical approach that a mathematician might adopt in this situation, rather than dive straight in at the deep end, is to ask himself the question:

Do you know a related problem?†

Let us adopt this approach ourselves. Certainly, the idea of coefficients occurs in a very different sort of field of mathematics – vectors, and we shall start there.

Suppose then, that we are given the vector $\mathbf{a} \in \mathbb{R}^3$ and have chosen the usual basis $\mathbf{e}_1, \mathbf{e}_2, \mathbf{e}_3$ for $\mathbb{R}^3$.

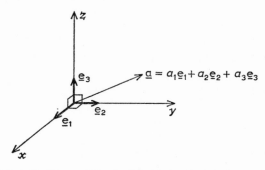

† See Polya, G. *How to Solve It.* (Doubleday Anchor Books) 1957.

We now want to extract from **a** its coefficient of e_2, for example. Of course the problem might never present itself in this way. Since **a** would probably be specified as (a_1, a_2, a_3), it is a trivial job to pick out a_2 as the coefficient of e_2. Let us suppose that this is not the case.

There is a property we can exploit. The particular basis vectors e_1, e_2, e_3 are *orthogonal*, that is to say

$$e_i . e_j = 0 \quad \text{if } i \neq j \text{ (see M.T.).}$$

Thus
$$a . e_2 = a_1 e_1 . e_2 + a_2 e_2 . e_2 + a_3 e_3 . e_2$$

$$= a_2 e_2 . e_2$$

and so
$$a_2 = \frac{a . e_2}{e_2 . e_2}.$$

What is more, in this particular case, not only are the basis vectors orthogonal, but they are of *unit length* and so

$$e_2 . e_2 = 1,$$

giving
$$a_2 = a . e_2.$$

Let us look at the way in which vectors are related to our original problem. If our approximation

$$f \simeq a_0 1 + a_1 \cos + b_1 \sin + a_2 \cos 2 + b_2 \sin 2 + \dots$$

is to be related to the equation

$$a = a_1 e_1 + a_2 e_2 + a_3 e_3$$

then we will have to find a way in which we can think of the set

$$\{1, \cos, \sin, \cos 2, \sin 2, \dots\}$$

as specifying a basis for a vector space of functions. We will then have to follow this up by defining a scalar product on the vector space in order to winkle out the coefficients a_0, a_1, b_1, a_2, b_2, ...

Let us take these two problems in the order in which they were stated.

Can the set of functions

$$\{1, \cos, \sin, \cos 2, \sin 2, \dots\}$$

be a basis for a vector space? If this were the case, then every member of this vector space would be expressible as a linear combination of this set. So let us define a set $\mathscr{F}$ by the rule

$$\mathscr{F} = \{\alpha_0 1 + \alpha_1 \cos + \alpha_2 \cos 2 + \ldots$$

$$+ \beta_1 \sin + \beta_2 \sin 2 + \ldots, \quad \text{where } \alpha_i, \beta_j \in \mathbf{R}\}.$$

Exercise 1

Show that if **f** and **g** are two functions in the set $\mathscr{F}$ then **f** + **g** and α**f** (where α is any real number) are functions in $\mathscr{F}$.

Exercise 1 shows us that we have two binary operations that are certainly candidates for making $\mathscr{F}$ into a vector space. In fact, it is not difficult to verify that $\mathscr{F}$ is a vector space. (For a detailed list of properties which have to be checked see M.T., Chapter 4T.)

Of course, we want more than that – we also require

$$\{1, \cos, \sin, \cos 2, \sin 2, \ldots\}$$

to be a basis for $\mathscr{F}$. For this to be possible, we put some restrictions on the type of functions that belong to $\mathscr{F}$. We shall be going into these restrictions in some detail in Chapter 4, but, for the moment, you can certainly see that for the function

$$\alpha_0 1 + \alpha_1 \cos + \alpha_2 \cos 2 + \ldots$$

$$+ \beta_1 \sin + \beta_2 \sin 2 +$$

to make sense, this series, for a start, must be convergent. What we mean by convergence of an infinite series of vectors is a bit mind-boggling, but that is one of the masochistic pleasures of the game!

We have shown how we can relate the functions to vectors by building up the vector space $\mathscr{F}$, which has the trigonometric functions as a basis. But can we define a scalar product on $\mathscr{F}$?

The way of defining a scalar product in $\mathbf{R}^3$ is by the rule

$$\mathbf{a}.\mathbf{b} = a_1 b_1 + a_2 b_2 + a_3 b_3.$$

We can express this rule as a mapping

$$. : (\mathbf{R}^3 \times \mathbf{R}^3) \to \mathbf{R}$$

such that $\qquad . : (\mathbf{a}, \mathbf{b}) \to a_1 b_1 + a_2 b_2 + a_3 b_3.$

15

This means that we are looking for a way of defining a scalar product on $\mathscr{F}$ so that it turns out to be a mapping

$$. : (\mathscr{F} \times \mathscr{F}) \to R.$$

Put into words, we need a mapping which maps pairs of functions to numbers. Now one mapping which maps functions to numbers is

$$\int_a^b : \text{(functions)} \to R.$$

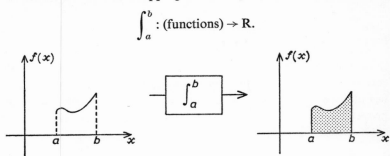

But the scalar product maps a *pair* of functions to a real number whereas the definite integral only maps single functions. Therefore, we need to find a way of combining two functions before we use the definite integral to map them to the real numbers. We could use any binary operation, but one in particular suggests itself for the following reason. For any vector **a**,

$$\mathbf{0}.\mathbf{a} = 0 \times a_1 + 0 \times a_2 + 0 \times a_3 = 0.$$

So we need a way of combining functions, $\square$ say, so that

$$\mathbf{0} \,\square\, \mathbf{f} = \mathbf{0}$$

where **0** is the zero function. The binary operation which does this for us is multiplication. This means that if **f** and **g** belong to $\mathscr{F}$, then we may do well to define the scalar product of **f** with **g** to be

$$\int_a^b f(x) \times g(x) \mathrm{d}x. \dagger$$

But what are a and b?

† This is one of the restrictions on the type of functions that belong to $\mathscr{F}$. For this to be a proper scalar product, whenever **f** and **g** belong to $\mathscr{F}$,

$$\int_a^b f(x)\, g(x)\, \mathrm{d}x$$

must exist.

In Chapter 1, we decided to use the periodic property of the trigonometric functions and to approximate functions over the domain $[-\pi, \pi]$. It seems natural, therefore, to choose

$$a = -\pi,$$
$$b = \pi,$$

and we shall soon see that it is a particularly apt choice. Having done this, we can make the definition of scalar product as follows

$$\mathbf{f.g} = \int_{-\pi}^{\pi} f(x) \times g(x) \mathrm{d}x.$$

This certainly looks like a scalar product. It has the two properties that we singled out; it maps a pair of functions to a real number, and $\mathbf{0.f} = 0$. But there are other properties of the scalar product in $\mathbf{R}^3$ that it would seem to be worth preserving. These are indicated in the following exercise.

Exercise 2

(i) In $\mathbf{R}^3$, $\mathbf{a.a} \geqslant 0$, and $\mathbf{a.a} = 0$ if and only if $\mathbf{a} = \mathbf{0}$. For our scalar product in $\mathscr{F}$, show that $\mathbf{f.f} \geqslant 0$, and $\mathbf{f.f} = 0$ if and only if $\mathbf{f} = \mathbf{0}$.

(ii) In $\mathbf{R}^3$, $\mathbf{a.b} = \mathbf{b.a}$. Show that, in $\mathscr{F}$, $\mathbf{f.g} = \mathbf{g.f}$.

(iii) Show that, in $\mathscr{F}$, $\mathbf{f.}(\alpha\mathbf{g}+\beta\mathbf{h}) = \alpha\mathbf{f.g}+\beta\mathbf{f.h}$ for any numbers α, β.

Exercise 3 (Optional)

Another property of the scalar product in $\mathbf{R}^3$ is that if θ is the angle between $\mathbf{a}$ and $\mathbf{b}$,

$$\cos\theta = \frac{\mathbf{a.b}}{\{(\mathbf{a.a})\,(\mathbf{b.b})\}^{\frac{1}{2}}}.$$

This means that $\dfrac{(\mathbf{a.b})^2}{(\mathbf{a.a})\,(\mathbf{b.b})} \leqslant 1.$

Show that if . is any scalar product with the properties of Exercise 2, in any vector space, then for any vectors $\mathbf{u}$ and $\mathbf{v}$ in that space

$$(\mathbf{u.v})^2 \leqslant (\mathbf{u.u})\,(\mathbf{v.v}).$$

[*Hint*. Consider $(\mathbf{u}+\lambda\mathbf{v}).(\mathbf{u}+\lambda\mathbf{v})$ and the result of Exercise 2(i).]

So the scalar product that we have found in $\mathscr{F}$ seems to justify the name scalar product, but it is not the only such scalar product we can define. Other mappings of $\mathscr{F} \times \mathscr{F}$ to $\mathbf{R}$ also have the properties we have noted in Exercise 2.

Exercise 4 (Optional)

Test each of the following definitions of . for the properties listed in Exercise 2.

(i) $\mathbf{f} . \mathbf{g} = \displaystyle\int_{-1}^{1} x f(x) g(x) \, dx;$

(ii) $\mathbf{f} . \mathbf{g} = \displaystyle\int_{0}^{\infty} e^{-x} f(x) g(x) \, dx;$

(iii) $\mathbf{f} . \mathbf{g} = \displaystyle\int_{-\infty}^{\infty} e^{-x^2} f(x) g(x) \, dx;$

where f and g are polynomial functions.

The reason we have singled out the special scalar product

$$\mathbf{f} . \mathbf{g} = \int_{-\pi}^{\pi} f(x) g(x) \, dx$$

is that it is going to give us the tool we need to solve the problem in hand. First, one might expect integration to come into the problem because, if you look back at the two diagrams on page 9, you will recall that we are interested in an approximation which is relevant over the whole domain, and integration *is* an operation which takes into account the behaviour of a function throughout its domain. Secondly, this particular inner product has a vitally important property. We have seen that, in R^3, the set $\{\mathbf{e}_1, \mathbf{e}_2, \mathbf{e}_3\}$ is orthogonal, and this led to the particularly easy way in which the coefficients of any vector could be picked out. In the same way the vectors $\{\mathbf{1}, \mathbf{cos}, \mathbf{sin}, \mathbf{cos2}, \mathbf{sin2}, ...\}$ are orthogonal in the sense that $\mathbf{f} . \mathbf{g} = \mathbf{0}$ whenever $\mathbf{f} \neq \mathbf{g}$. This result is so important to our purposes that it is worth expressing as a theorem.

THEOREM 2.1

With scalar product defined on the set $\mathscr{F}$ by the rule

$$\mathbf{f} . \mathbf{g} = \int_{-\pi}^{\pi} f(x) g(x) \, dx$$

the basis set $\{\mathbf{1}, \mathbf{cos}, \mathbf{sin}, \mathbf{cos2}, \mathbf{sin2}, ..., \mathbf{cosr}, \mathbf{sinr}, ...\}$ is orthogonal.

Proof

(i) $\mathbf{1.cos\,r} = \displaystyle\int_{-\pi}^{\pi} \cos(rx)\mathrm{d}x$ for $r \in Z^+$, the set of positive integers,

$$= \left[\frac{1}{r}\sin(rx)\right]_{-\pi}^{\pi}$$

$$= 0, \quad \text{since } \sin(r\pi) = 0.$$

(ii) $\mathbf{1.sin\,r} = \displaystyle\int_{-\pi}^{\pi} \sin(rx)\mathrm{d}x$ for $r \in Z^+$

$$= \left[-\frac{1}{r}\cos(rx)\right]_{-\pi}^{\pi}$$

$$= 0, \quad \text{since } \cos\theta = \cos(-\theta).$$

(iii) $\mathbf{cos\,p.cos\,r} = \displaystyle\int_{-\pi}^{\pi} \cos(px)\cos(rx)\mathrm{d}x$ $(p \neq r \text{ and } p, r \in Z^+)$

$$= \int_{-\pi}^{\pi} \tfrac{1}{2}(\cos(p+r)x + \cos(p-r)x)\mathrm{d}x$$

$$= 0$$

since if we evaluate the two parts of the integral separately, we have integrals like those in (i).

(iv) $\mathbf{sin\,p.sin\,r} = \displaystyle\int_{-\pi}^{\pi} \sin(px)\sin(rx)\mathrm{d}x$ $(p \neq r \text{ and } p, r \in Z^+)$

$$= \int_{-\pi}^{\pi} \tfrac{1}{2}(\cos(p-r)\,x - \cos(p+r)\,x)\mathrm{d}x$$

$$= 0$$

again as in (i).

(v) $\mathbf{cos\,p.sin\,r} = \displaystyle\int_{-\pi}^{\pi} \cos(px)\sin(rx)\mathrm{d}x$ $(p, r \in Z^+)$

$$= \int_{-\pi}^{\pi} \tfrac{1}{2}(\sin(p+r)x + \sin(r-p)x)\mathrm{d}x$$

$$= 0$$

since the two parts of the integral are like (ii) above, even if $p = r$.

Gathering together the results of (i) to (v), we see that if **f** and **g** are any elements of the basis set **1, cos, sin, cos2, sin2**, ..., then if

$$\mathbf{f} \neq \mathbf{g},$$

$$\mathbf{f} . \mathbf{g} = 0.$$

With proof of this theorem, we have found that we can define a scalar product in a satisfactory manner. The fact that the basis is an orthogonal set is particularly helpful in our later discussions. One final property that we can find in the set of vectors $\{\mathbf{e_1}, \mathbf{e_2}, \mathbf{e_3}\}$ is that

$$\mathbf{e}_i . \mathbf{e}_i = 1 \quad \text{for } i = 1, 2, 3.$$

Our basis for $\mathscr{F}$ does not have this property, but that is not the end of the world. We leave it to you to find the values of **f.f**, in the next exercise.

Exercise 5

Prove the following results.

(i) $\mathbf{1.1} = 2\pi$;
(ii) $\mathbf{cos\,m.cos\,m} = \pi$ for $m \in Z^+$;
(iii) $\mathbf{sin\,n.sin\,n} = \pi$ for $n \in Z^+$.

Having related trigonometric functions to vectors, let us now exploit this way of looking at things. The technique for finding coefficients of the vector **a** was typified by the result

$$\mathbf{a} . \mathbf{e_2} = a_2.$$

We can use this method for finding coefficients in the 'equation'

$$\mathbf{f} \simeq a_0\mathbf{1} + a_1\mathbf{cos} + b_1\mathbf{sin} + a_2\mathbf{cos2} + b_2\mathbf{sin2} + \ldots.$$

Suppose we want to find a_2, the coefficient of **cos2**, and suppose further for the moment that we are justified in replacing $\simeq$ by $=$. We then have

$$\mathbf{f} . \mathbf{cos2} = a_0\mathbf{1}.\mathbf{cos2} + a_1\mathbf{cos}.\mathbf{cos2} + b_1\mathbf{sin}.\mathbf{cos2} + a_2\mathbf{cos2}.\mathbf{cos2}$$

$$+ b_2\mathbf{sin2}.\mathbf{cos2} + \ldots$$

$$= a_0 \times 0 + a_1 \times 0 + b_1 \times 0 + a_2 \times \pi + b_2 \times 0 + \ldots$$

$$= \pi a_2.$$

This means that we can find a_2 from the equation

$$a_2 = \frac{1}{\pi} \int_{-\pi}^{\pi} f(x) \cos 2x \, \mathrm{d}x$$

so long as we can evaluate the integral. If we can use this method to find all the coefficients a_i, b_i, then we will obtain an approximation to **f** and this is the particular approximation which we have called the Fourier Series for **f**. We can then investigate how good the approximation is.

Summary of Chapter 2

We have defined a scalar product on the set $\mathscr{F}$ by the rule

$$\mathbf{f}.\mathbf{g} = \int_{-\pi}^{\pi} f(x) g(x) \, \mathrm{d}x.$$

Using this definition of scalar product, we proved Theorem 2.1.

The basis set of $\mathscr{F}$, $\{\mathbf{1}, \cos, \sin, \cos 2, \sin 2, \ldots\}$ is orthogonal.

This result helped us to show that the Fourier coefficient a_2 of **f** could be found as follows:

$$a_2 = \frac{1}{\pi} \mathbf{f}.\cos 2.$$

In the next chapter we extend this result to finding all the Fourier coefficients of **f**.

3 · Finding Fourier Series

Because the trigonometric functions form an orthogonal basis for $\mathscr{F}$, we can develop a procedure for calculating Fourier Series. The procedure can be extended to functions which are not periodic and defined on a general interval $[a, b]$. Odd and even functions have particularly interesting properties in this context.

In this chapter we shall consolidate the results of Chapter 2 by looking at some examples of Fourier Series. The examples we choose are rather simple – and somewhat contrived. This is done deliberately, for it is important to see how a new method works before trying it on complicated applications.

Following the theorem of Chapter 2, we can adopt a procedure for finding a Fourier Series of a given function. As long as one can perform the necessary integration, the Fourier coefficients are given by

$$\mathbf{f.1} = \int_{-\pi}^{\pi} f(x)\,\mathrm{d}x = \int_{-\pi}^{\pi} a_0 \times 1\,\mathrm{d}x = 2\pi a_0$$

$$\mathbf{f.\cos m} = \int_{-\pi}^{\pi} f(x)\cos mx\,\mathrm{d}x = \int_{-\pi}^{\pi} a_m \cos^2 mx\,\mathrm{d}x = \pi a_m$$

$$\mathbf{f.\sin n} = \int_{-\pi}^{\pi} f(x)\sin nx\,\mathrm{d}x = \int_{-\pi}^{\pi} b_n \sin^2 nx\,\mathrm{d}x = \pi b_n.$$

So we suggest the following procedure for evaluating Fourier coefficients.

Step 1. Evaluate the integral $a_0 = \dfrac{1}{2\pi} \int_{-\pi}^{\pi} f(x)\,\mathrm{d}x$.

Step 2. Evaluate the integral $a_m = \dfrac{1}{\pi} \int_{-\pi}^{\pi} f(x)\cos mx\,\mathrm{d}x$.

Step. 3. Evaluate the integral $b_n = \dfrac{1}{\pi} \int_{-\pi}^{\pi} f(x)\,\sin nx\,\mathrm{d}x$.

We can then substitute the results of Steps 1–3 into the expression

$$a_0 1 + a_1 \cos + b_1 \sin + a_2 \cos 2 + b_2 \sin 2 + \dots$$

to get the Fourier Series for **f**.

Notice at this point that, as long as one can evaluate the integrals, then one can always find the Fourier Series of a given function. However, we are not yet sure whether or not the Fourier Series has any meaning. That is, we do not know whether or not, as an approximation to **f**, the Fourier Series is at all successful. For the moment, we shall take this success of approximation on trust, but it clearly needs investigating and we shall go into it in Chapter 4.

Example 1

Find the Fourier Series of the function **f** which is defined by

$$\mathbf{f}: x \to x \quad (x \in [-\pi, \pi]).$$

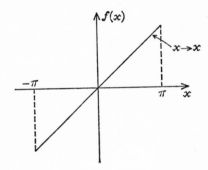

Solution

Following the procedure suggested above, we need to calculate

Step 1 $a_0 = \dfrac{1}{2\pi} \displaystyle\int_{-\pi}^{\pi} x\,\mathrm{d}x.$

Step 2 $a_m = \dfrac{1}{\pi} \displaystyle\int_{-\pi}^{\pi} x\cos mx\,\mathrm{d}x.$

Step 3 $b_n = \dfrac{1}{\pi} \displaystyle\int_{-\pi}^{\pi} x\sin nx\,\mathrm{d}x.$

We can effect a rather dramatic saving in labour if we recall (see M.T.) that if g is an odd function, then

$$\int_{-a}^{a} g = 0.$$

23

This means that we know straight away that a_0 and a_m are zero since $x \to x$ and $x \to x\cos mx$ are odd functions. This leaves only

Step 3 $b_n = \dfrac{1}{\pi} \displaystyle\int_{-\pi}^{\pi} f(x)\sin nx\, dx$

$= \dfrac{1}{\pi} \displaystyle\int_{-\pi}^{\pi} x\sin nx\, dx$

and we have to use integration by parts.

$$b_n = \frac{1}{\pi}\left[-\frac{x}{n}\cos nx\right]_{-\pi}^{\pi} - \frac{1}{\pi}\int_{-\pi}^{\pi} -\frac{1}{n}\cos nx\, dx$$

$$= \frac{1}{\pi}\left[-\frac{x}{n}\cos nx + \frac{1}{n^2}\sin nx\right]_{-\pi}^{\pi}.$$

From the following graphs, you can probably see that

$$\sin(n\pi) = 0$$

and $$\cos(n\pi) = (-1)^n,$$

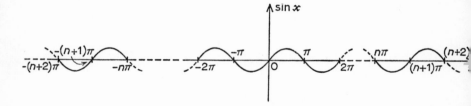

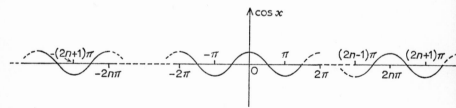

so it follows that

$$b_n = \frac{1}{\pi}\left\{-\frac{\pi}{n}(-1)^n + \frac{-\pi}{n}(-1)^n + 0 - 0\right\},$$

$$\boxed{b_n = \frac{2}{n}(-1)^{n+1}.}$$

We have now found the Fourier coefficients, and we can substitute our results into the general form of the Fourier Series to get

$$\mathbf{f} \simeq 2\left(\sin-\frac{\sin2}{2}+\frac{\sin3}{3}-\frac{\sin4}{4}+\ldots\right).$$

Post-mortem

Having gone to such lengths to approximate a perfectly simple function, $\mathbf{f}: x \to x$, by a rather complicated one, the following graphs show how successful we have been in the attempt.

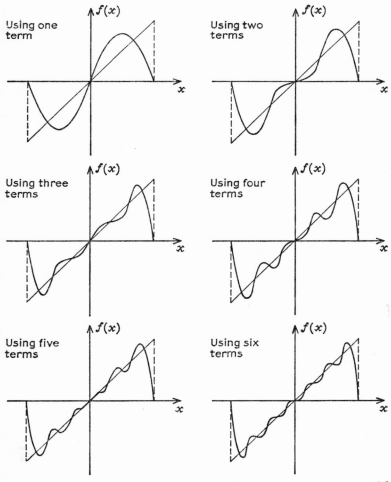

Using one term

Using two terms

Using three terms

Using four terms

Using five terms

Using six terms

The point to notice in these diagrams is that the more terms of the approximation that we use, the more 'reasonable' the approximation to **f** seems to become. The sudden dip at the end of the interval, $x = \pi$, does seem to be rather a problem – we shall be discussing this in the next chapter.

Example 2

Find the Fourier Series of the function **g** which is defined by

$$\mathbf{g}\colon x \to x^2 \quad (x \in [-\pi, \pi]).$$

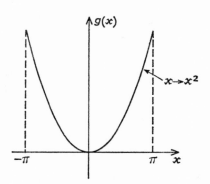

Solution

Step 1 $a_0 = \dfrac{1}{2\pi} \displaystyle\int_{-\pi}^{\pi} x^2 \, dx$

$$= \frac{1}{2\pi} \left[\frac{1}{3} x^3 + c \right]_{-\pi}^{\pi}$$

$$\boxed{a_0 = \frac{\pi^2}{3}.}$$

Step 2 $a_m = \dfrac{1}{\pi} \displaystyle\int_{-\pi}^{\pi} x^2 \cos mx \, dx$

and we have to use two applications of integration by parts to evaluate this integral.

26

$$a_m = \frac{1}{\pi}\left[\frac{x^2}{m}\sin mx\right]_{-\pi}^{\pi} - \frac{1}{\pi}\int_{-\pi}^{\pi}\frac{2x}{m}\sin mx\,\mathrm{d}x$$

$$= \frac{1}{\pi}\left[\frac{x^2}{m}\sin mx + \frac{2x}{m^2}\cos mx\right]_{-\pi}^{\pi} - \frac{1}{\pi}\int_{-\pi}^{\pi}\frac{2}{m^2}\cos mx\,\mathrm{d}x$$

$$= \frac{1}{\pi}\left[\frac{x^2}{m}\sin mx + \frac{2x}{m^2}\cos mx - \frac{2}{m^3}\sin mx\right]_{-\pi}^{\pi}$$

and using the results that

$$\sin m\pi = 0$$

and
$$\cos m\pi = (-1)^m,$$

we find that

$$\boxed{a_m = \frac{4}{m^2}(-1)^m.}$$

Step 3 $b_n = \frac{1}{\pi}\int_{-\pi}^{\pi} x^2\sin nx\,\mathrm{d}x.$

As in Example 1, we have the integral of an odd function with limits $-\pi$ and π, so

$$\boxed{b_n = 0.}$$

Substituting these values for the Fourier coefficients into the Fourier Series, we get

$$\mathbf{g} \simeq \frac{\pi^2}{3}\,\mathbf{1} - \frac{4}{1^2}\cos + \frac{4}{2^2}\cos 2 - \frac{4}{3^2}\cos 3 + \dots,$$

which we can write as

$$\mathbf{g} \simeq \frac{\pi^2}{3}\mathbf{1} - 4\left(\cos - \frac{\cos 2}{2^2} + \frac{\cos 3}{3^2} - \dots\right).$$

Notice that we need to retain the function **1** in this expression, since we have an approximation which links two functions. The corresponding approximation which links the images of the functions is

$$g(x) \simeq \frac{\pi^2}{3} - 4\left(\cos x - \frac{\cos 2x}{2^2} + \frac{\cos 3x}{3^2} - \dots\right) \quad (x \in [-\pi, \pi]).$$

In this 'equation', we must be particularly careful to specify the set of values which x can take, since, on the face of it, we can substitute $x = 2\pi$ in each side, but 2π is not in the domain of **g**. In fact, we know that to put $x = 2\pi$ would give nonsense. For the right-hand side has the same value at $x = 0$ as it has at $x = 2\pi$, but this is not the same for $g(x)$; $(0)^2$ is certainly not the same as $(2\pi)^2$. As we remarked in Chapter 1, when we find a Fourier Series we take it as assured that the approximation is intended to apply only at points in the domain of the function to be approximated, even though the Fourier Series itself has domain R.

Post-mortem

The following graphs show how successful the approximation has been.

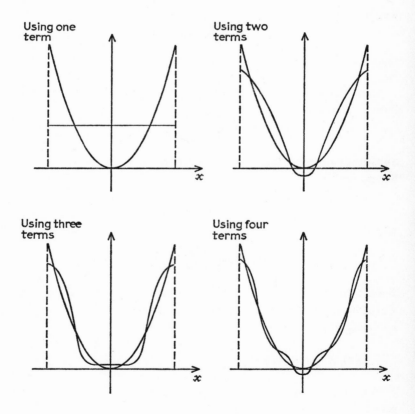

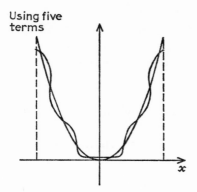

Using five terms

Even though the approximation obtained by using one or two terms of the series is rather poor, by the time we have five terms the accuracy seems to be greatly improved.

Exercise 1

Find Fourier Series for the following functions:

(i) $f: x \to 2x$ $(x \in [-\pi, \pi])$;
(ii) $f: x \to 3$ $(x \in [-\pi, \pi])$;
(iii) $f: x \to x^2 + 1$ $(x \in [-\pi, \pi])$;
(iv) $f: x \to x^3 + x$ $(x \in [-\pi, \pi])$.

Exercise 2

(i) By putting $x = \frac{1}{2}\pi$ in the answer to Example 1, obtain the formula

$$\tfrac{1}{4}\pi = 1 - \tfrac{1}{3} + \tfrac{1}{5} - \tfrac{1}{7} + \dots.$$

This formula is known as Gregory's Formula. How many terms of this formula would you have to take to calculate π correct to 4 decimal places?

(ii) By putting $x = \frac{1}{2}\pi$ in the answer to Example 2 obtain the formula

$$\frac{\pi^2}{12} = 1 - \frac{1}{2^2} + \frac{1}{3^2} - \frac{1}{4^2} + \dots.$$

How many terms of this sequence are needed to give π correct to 4 decimal places?

In Examples 1 and 2, and in the results of the exercises, you may have noticed that, in some instances, all the functions of the type **cos m** dropped out (i.e. $a_m = 0$) of the Fourier Series for a given function. In other cases, it was the **sin n** functions which dropped out.

29

But, at least it has been a case of 'One out, all out!' In fact, it is easy to predict in advance of our finding the coefficients, which functions, if any, will drop out.

In Example 1, the function whose Fourier Series we found was

$$\mathbf{f}\colon x \to x \quad (x \in [-\pi, \pi]),$$

and the functions which dropped out of the Fourier Series were the **cos**m functions. We were left with the **sin**n functions in the approximation to **f**. In Example 2, the function was

$$\mathbf{g}\colon x \to x^2 \quad (x \in [-\pi, \pi]).$$

This time the drop-outs were the **sin**n functions, and we were left with the **cos**m functions in the approximation to **g** – remember that **1** can be thought of as being the **cos**0 function. The reason that the relevant integrals were zero was that

> **f** is an odd function

and **g** is an even function.

Exercise 3

Any function **f** can be expressed as the sum of an odd function and an even function. Consider the two functions $\mathbf{O}_f$ and $\mathbf{E}_f$ defined by

$$O_f(x) = \frac{f(x) - f(-x)}{2},$$

$$E_f(x) = \frac{f(x) + f(-x)}{2}.$$

Show that $\mathbf{O}_f$ is odd, $\mathbf{E}_f$ is even and express **f** in terms of $\mathbf{O}_f$ and $\mathbf{E}_f$.

We might suspect then, that when we represent a function by its Fourier Series, the sine terms represent the odd part of the function, and the cosine terms represent the even part of the function (see Exercise 4). Further, if **f** is an odd function, we might suspect that it *cannot* have any even functions in its expansion, for we know that the sum of an odd and an even function is neither odd nor even. Similarly, if **g** is an even function, we might suspect that it cannot have any odd functions in its expansion. However, we so far know only about adding together *two* functions, a result which we can generalise to adding any finite number, but not to an infinite number of functions as we are trying to do. However, these suspicions can be proved directly from our formulae for the coefficients, as in the following theorems.

THEOREM 3.1

If **f** is an odd function, then its Fourier Series contains only functions of the type **sin n**.

Proof

Consider the procedure for finding the Fourier coefficients of **f**.

Step 1 $a_0 = \dfrac{1}{2\pi} \displaystyle\int_{-\pi}^{\pi} f(x)\,\mathrm{d}x = 0$
because f is odd.

$$\boxed{a_0 = 0.}$$

Step 2 $a_m = \dfrac{1}{\pi} \displaystyle\int_{-\pi}^{\pi} f(x)\cos mx\,\mathrm{d}x$

which is the integral of the product of an odd and an even function, that is to say, it is the integral of an odd function, with limits $-\pi$ and π. Thus

$$\boxed{a_m = 0.}$$

So that when we substitute these Fourier coefficients into the Fourier Series for **f**, all that we are left with is

$$\mathbf{f} \simeq b_1\sin + b_2\sin 2 + b_3\sin 3 + \dots$$

as required.

A further point comes from the last step of the procedure for finding the Fourier coefficients.

Step 3 $b_n = \displaystyle\int_{-\pi}^{\pi} f(x)\sin nx\,\mathrm{d}x.$

If **f** is an odd function, then we have the integral of an even function between $-\pi$ and π. So we can find b_n in the following way.

$$b_n = \frac{2}{\pi} \int_{0}^{\pi} f(x)\sin nx\,\mathrm{d}x.$$

The same sort of results hold for even functions, and since the proof

31

is very similar to the proof of Theorem 3.1, it is left as an exercise for you to do.

THEOREM 3.2

If **g** is an even function, then its Fourier Series consists only of functions of the type **cos m**.

Exercise 4

Prove Theorem 3.2 by obtaining a similar result for b_n and even functions as we obtained above for a_m and odd functions.

We can use the results of these last two theorems to save ourselves a lot of effort when working out Fourier coefficients for odd or even functions. For, as soon as we know that a function is either odd or even, we can predict which of the coefficients will be zero, without having to do any integration.

Exercise 5

Find the Fourier Series of the following functions.

    (i) $f: x \to |x|$ $(x \in [-\pi, \pi])$;

    (ii) $f: x \to e^{|x|}$ $(x \in [-\pi, \pi])$;

    (iii) $f: x \to (\pi - x)(\pi + x)$ $(x \in [-\pi, \pi])$.

You may wonder why we put this emphasis on odd and even functions, after all, even though they seem convenient, the chance that a random function will be odd or even is rather remote. But it so happens that in practical applications one can often choose a function to be odd or even.

All the examples considered so far have involved some function whose domain is $[-\pi, \pi]$. This choice of domain was important. In particular, the result that the basis of $\mathscr{F}$,

$$\{1, \cos, \sin, \cos 2, \sin 2, \ldots\},$$

is an orthogonal set depends upon it. But many functions are not obliging enough to have the interval $[-\pi, \pi]$ for domain, or to be periodic with period 2π. Fourier Series, however, are applicable to a more general class of functions as we indicated at the end of Chapter 1. So we shall look now to see how we can modify our procedures to cope with functions defined on different domains. We shall first consider only a slight alteration to the domain $[-\pi, \pi]$, by making it $[0, \pi]$, and go on to look at more general cases. To keep on familiar territory, let us look again at Example 1.

In Example 1, the function was

$$\mathbf{f}: x \to x \quad (x \in [-\pi, \pi]).$$

We shall now consider the new function

$$\mathbf{f}_1: x \to x \quad (x \in [0, \pi]).$$

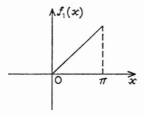

We have at least two options open to us. First, we could regard this as a case of a function defined over an interval of length $L \neq 2\pi$. Second, since the length of the interval is simply related to 2π, we could extend the function in some way so that the domain of the extended function *is* $[-\pi, \pi]$, and the original function and the extended function coincide on $[0, \pi]$.

The first option is covered by the general case of functions with domain an interval of length not equal to 2π which we shall deal with later. The second option takes advantages of the special nature of the problem, and to see just what these advantages are we shall follow up this particular approach.

We can extend the function $\mathbf{f}_1$ in various ways. For example the function $\mathbf{f}_2$ with the following graph

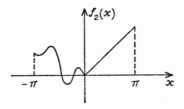

coincides with $\mathbf{f}_1$ over the interval $[0, \pi]$ and so the Fourier Series for $\mathbf{f}_2$ serves as an approximation to $\mathbf{f}_1$ in $[0, \pi]$. But there is no point in making such an arbitrary extension. It *is* sensible, however to extend f_1 to a new function which is either odd or even.

If we want to extend f_1 to be an odd function, then we define the new function f_2 by

$$f_2(x) = f_1(x) \qquad \text{for} \quad (x \in [0, \pi]),$$
$$f_2(x) = -f_1(-x) \quad \text{for} \quad (x \in [-\pi, 0]).$$

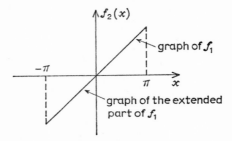

This is just the function we had in Example 1. On the other hand, we would get f_2 to be an even function if we were to define

$$f_2(x) = f_1(x) \qquad \text{for} \quad (x \in [0, \pi]),$$
$$f_2(x) = f_1(-x) \qquad \text{for} \quad (x \in [-\pi, 0]).$$

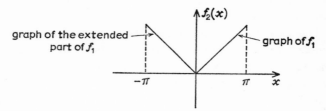

Exercise 6

Find the Fourier Series of the function

$$f_1: x \to x \quad (x \in [0, \pi])$$

having extended the domain of f_1 to be $[-\pi, \pi]$ to give

    (i) an odd function;

    (ii) an even function.

You should get very different results for parts (i) and (ii) of this exercise, but then the graphs over the extended interval are rather different.

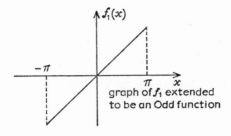

graph of f_1 extended
to be an Odd function

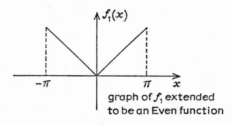

graph of f_1 extended
to be an Even function

It is clear that for functions with domain $[0, \pi]$ one can obtain as many different Fourier Series as the number of extensions to the function we like to consider. It may seen strange to you that one can get different series approximating to the same function, but it is only a sophisticated version of the fact that many different numerical series can converge to the same limit.

Because of their simplicity, the Fourier Series obtained by extending a function **f** to an even or odd function are particularly useful. They are given special names, the *Fourier Cosine Series* for **f** and the *Fourier Sine Series* for **f**.

Exercise 7

   (i) If g_1 is the function

$$g_1: x \to x^2 \quad (x \in [0, \pi]),$$

find (*a*) the Fourier Cosine Series for g_1, and (*b*) the Fourier Sine Series for g_1.

   (ii) Use the Fourier Cosine Series in Exercise 6 to get the formula

$$\frac{\pi^2}{8} = 1 + \frac{1}{3^2} + \frac{1}{5^2} + \frac{1}{7^2} + \dots.$$

Exercise 8

    (i) Find the Fourier Sine Series for the function

$$x \to \cos x \quad (x \in [0, \pi]).$$

    (ii) Find the Fourier Cosine Series for the function

$$x \to \sin x \quad (x \in [0, \pi]).$$

    (iii) Do the results of (i) and (ii) above mean that the set

$$\{\mathbf{1, \cos, \sin, \cos 2, \sin 2, ...}\}$$

is *not* linearly independent? Explain your answer.

So far, our functions have been defined on an interval. But the **cos m** and **sin n** functions are defined for all $x \in$ R. What happens if we lift the restriction on the domain of the Fourier Series? On page 28, we noted that if we move outside the interval $[-\pi, \pi]$ then the Fourier Series no longer approximates to the given function. Thus we cannot infer from the Fourier Series for $x \to x^2$, $x \in [-\pi, \pi]$ that

$$(2\pi)^2 = \frac{\pi^2}{3} - 4\left(1 - \frac{1}{2^2} + \frac{1}{3^2} - ...\right).$$

But it would seem natural to ask what function, if any, the Fourier Series approximates to outside this interval. Well, Fourier Series involve the sine and cosine functions and the important feature of these functions here is that they are periodic, with period 2π. This property tells us that whatever values the Fourier Series takes on, the interval $[-\pi, \pi]$ will be repeated over each interval

$$[-\pi + 2k\pi, \pi + 2k\pi] \quad \text{for} \quad k \in Z.$$

Suppose, then, that we take the function of Example 1,

$$\mathbf{f}: x \to x \quad (x \in [-\pi, \pi]).$$

We can extend the domain of **f**, and keep the property that the Fourier Series approximates **f** if we define a function $\mathbf{f_1}$ which has period 2π and which coincides with **f** on $-[\pi, \pi]$. If we do this, then the graph of $\mathbf{f_1}$ will be as follows.

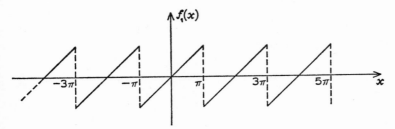

Similarly, we can take the function of Example 2,

$$\mathbf{g}: x \to x^2 \quad (x \in [-\pi, \pi]),$$

and define $\mathbf{g_1}$ in such a way that $\mathbf{g_1}$ coincides with $\mathbf{g}$ on $[-\pi, \pi]$ and has period 2π. The graph of $\mathbf{g_1}$ will be the following.

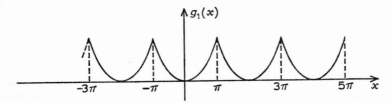

When $\mathbf{f}$ and $\mathbf{g}$ have been extended in this manner, then we know that their respective Fourier Series approximate to them in $[-\pi, \pi]$ and will approximate to $\mathbf{f_1}$ and $\mathbf{g_1}$ for all values of $x \in \mathbb{R}$. Another generalization comes from the results of the following exercise.

Exercise 9

(i) Show that, with scalar product defined by the rule

$$\mathbf{f} \cdot \mathbf{g} = \int_{-L}^{L} f(x)g(x)\,\mathrm{d}x,$$

the set $\left\{1, \cos\dfrac{\pi}{L}, \sin\dfrac{\pi}{L}, \cos\dfrac{2\pi}{L}, \sin\dfrac{2\pi}{L}, \ldots, \cos\dfrac{r\pi}{L}, \sin\dfrac{r\pi}{L}, \ldots\right\}$ is orthogonal

(see Theorem 2.1).

(ii) Show that

$$\cos\frac{m\pi}{L} \cdot \cos\frac{m\pi}{L} = L \quad \text{for} \quad m = 1, 2, \ldots$$

$$\sin\frac{n\pi}{L} \cdot \sin\frac{n\pi}{L} = L \quad \text{for} \quad n = 1, 2, \ldots$$

37

Using the results of this exercise, we can extend the application of Fourier Series to functions whose domains are $[-L, L]$. We do this by using the set of functions

$$\left\{1, \cos\frac{\pi}{L}, \sin\frac{\pi}{L}, \cos\frac{2\pi}{L}, \sin\frac{2\pi}{L}, \ldots\right\}$$

as the basis for a space of functions. The procedure for finding Fourier coefficients has to be slightly modified. It becomes

Step 1 $a_0 = \dfrac{1}{2L}\displaystyle\int_{-L}^{L} f(x)\,\mathrm{d}x.$

Step 2 $a_m = \dfrac{1}{L}\displaystyle\int_{-L}^{L} f(x)\cos\frac{m\pi x}{L}\,\mathrm{d}x.$

Step 3 $b_n = \dfrac{1}{L}\displaystyle\int_{-L}^{L} f(x)\sin\frac{n\pi x}{L}\,\mathrm{d}x$

and then substitute these coefficients in the series

$$a_0 1 + a_1\cos\frac{\pi}{L} + b_1\sin\frac{\pi}{L} + a_2\cos\frac{2\pi}{L} + b_2\sin\frac{2\pi}{L} + \ldots$$

Note that, if we put $L = \pi$, this procedure is the same as the original procedure given on page 22. Also, the same properties of odd and even functions apply.

Example 3

Find the Fourier Series of the function **f** defined by

$$\mathbf{f}\colon x \to |x| \quad (x \in [-L, L]).$$

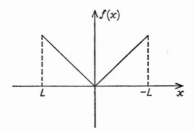

Solution

The modulus function is an even function, and so we know that $b_n = 0$ for all $n \in Z^+$. Using the properties of even functions,

38

Step 1 $a_0 = \dfrac{2}{2L} \displaystyle\int_0^L x \, dx$

$\qquad = \dfrac{L}{2}.$

Step 2 $a_m = \dfrac{2}{L} \displaystyle\int_0^L x \cos \dfrac{m\pi x}{L} \, dx$

$\qquad = \dfrac{2}{L} \left[\dfrac{Lx}{m\pi} \sin \dfrac{m\pi x}{L} \right]_0^L - \dfrac{2}{L} \displaystyle\int_0^L \dfrac{L}{m\pi} \sin \dfrac{m\pi x}{L} \, dx$

$\qquad = \dfrac{2}{L} \left[\dfrac{Lx}{m\pi} \sin \dfrac{m\pi x}{L} + \dfrac{L^2}{m^2\pi^2} \cos \dfrac{m\pi x}{L} \right]_0^L$

$\qquad = \dfrac{2L}{m^2\pi^2} \left((-1)^m - 1 \right).$

So that
$$a_m = \begin{cases} 0 & \text{if } m \text{ is even}, \, m \neq 0, \\ \dfrac{-4L}{m^2\pi^2} & \text{if } m \text{ is odd}. \end{cases}$$

Hence we get the Fourier Series

$$|x| \simeq \dfrac{L}{2} - \dfrac{4L}{\pi^2} \left\{ \cos\left(\dfrac{\pi x}{L}\right) + \dfrac{\cos\left(\dfrac{3\pi x}{L}\right)}{3^2} + \dfrac{\cos\left(\dfrac{5\pi x}{L}\right)}{5^2} + \ldots \right\} \quad (x \in [-L, L]).$$

Using this Fourier Series for **f**, we see that we can extend **f** to a function $\mathbf{f_1}$ so that the Fourier Series approximates to $\mathbf{f_1}$ for all values of $x \in$ R. The extended function has the following graph.

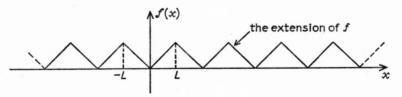

For this function, as with all periodic functions, whatever value $a \in$ R that we choose, the graph of the function repeats the pattern made in the interval $[a, a+2L]$ at regular intervals of length $2L$. But it does not matter where we start the interval $[a, a+2L]$, the pattern of the graph is repeated in the interval $[a+2L, a+4L]$, again in the interval $[a+4L, a+6L]$, and so on.

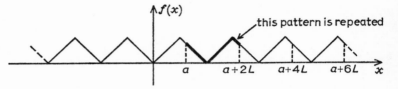

This repetition of pattern suggests that we could get a more general result if, instead of centering our interval of integration about 0, we might try defining scalar product by the rule

$$\mathbf{f}.\mathbf{g} = \int_{a}^{a+2L} f(x)g(x)\,\mathrm{d}x.$$

This generalization turns out to be perfectly valid as the results of the following exercise show.

Exercise 10

(i) Show that with scalar product defined by

$$\mathbf{f}.\mathbf{g} = \int_{a}^{a+2L} f(x)\,g(x)\,\mathrm{d}x$$

the set $\left\{1, \cos\dfrac{\pi}{L}, \sin\dfrac{\pi}{L}, \cos\dfrac{2\pi}{L}, \sin\dfrac{2\pi}{L}, ..., \cos\dfrac{r\pi}{L}, \sin\dfrac{r\pi}{L}, ...\right\}$ is orthogonal.

(ii) Show that $\qquad \mathbf{1}.\mathbf{1} = 2L,$

$$\cos\frac{m\pi}{L}.\cos\frac{m\pi}{L} = L \quad \text{for} \quad m = 1, 2, ...,$$

$$\sin\frac{n\pi}{L}.\sin\frac{n\pi}{L} = L \quad \text{for} \quad n = 1, 2, ...$$

The results of this exercise enable us to find the Fourier Series of a function whose domain is the general interval $[a, b]$. We choose L so that

$$b = a+2L,$$

i.e.

$$L = \frac{b-a}{2},$$

and we can define a scalar product by the rule

$$\mathbf{f}.\mathbf{g} = \int_{a}^{b} f(x)g(x)\,\mathrm{d}x.$$

With this scalar product, the results of Exercise 10 tell us that the set

$$\left\{1, \cos\frac{2\pi}{b-a}, \sin\frac{2\pi}{b-a}, \cos\frac{4\pi}{b-a}, \sin\frac{4\pi}{b-a}, \ldots\right\}$$

is orthogonal. We can also modify our procedure to take account of the changes that have been made.

Step 1 $a_0 = \dfrac{1}{b-a}\displaystyle\int_a^b f(x)\,dx.$

Step 2 $a_m = \dfrac{2}{b-a}\displaystyle\int_a^b f(x)\cos\frac{2m\pi x}{b-a}\,dx.$

Step 3 $b_n = \dfrac{2}{b-a}\displaystyle\int_a^b f(x)\sin\frac{2n\pi x}{b-a}\,dx$

and then substitute the coefficients in the series

$$a_0 + a_1\cos\left(\frac{2\pi x}{b-a}\right) + a_2\cos\left(\frac{4\pi x}{b-a}\right) + \ldots$$

$$+ b_1\sin\left(\frac{3\pi x}{b-a}\right) + b_2\sin\left(\frac{4\pi x}{b-a}\right) + \ldots.$$

Again, the Fourier Series defines a function whose domain could be taken to be the whole of the real line R and which has period $b-a$. Thus if the Fourier Series approximates to **f** in $[a, b]$, it approximates to the extended (periodic) function $\mathbf{f}_1$, for all values of $x \in$ R.

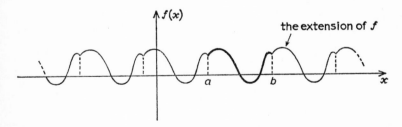

We can also work from the other angle. That is, we can start with a function **f** with domain R which we know to be periodic with period $2L$, say. We can then find the Fourier Series of **f** by taking scalar product to be

$$\mathbf{f}.\mathbf{g} = \int_{-L}^{L} f(x)g(x)\,dx.$$

41

FOURIER SERIES

The Fourier Series will approximate to **f** for all values $x \in \mathbb{R}$. We do not even need to choose $[-L, L]$ as the interval over which to make the first approximation. It might be more convenient to take $[a, a+2L]$ to be the interval for some suitable value of a, and, of course, one particular value of a which proves useful in many cases is $a = 0$. In this case, we take our scalar product to be

$$\int_0^{2L} f(x)g(x)\,\mathrm{d}x.$$

Having seen how to extend the application of Fourier Series to functions with domain $[a, b]$, we can return to functions with domain $[-\pi, \pi]$.

The results that we have obtained for $[a, b]$ type functions are so similar to the results obtained previously, give or take a few constants, that it is easy to generalise further results about functions with domains $[-\pi, \pi]$. In fact, by concentrating on these latter functions, the extra constants, which tend to make the results look so complicated are removed and one stands a chance of seeing the wood for the trees! So from now on, we shall concentrate once more on functions with domain $[-\pi, \pi]$ or $[0, \pi]$.

Let us take a look at one more example. So far, we have discussed only functions which are continuous; this time we have a function which is not continuous.

Example 4

Find the Fourier Series of the function **f** which is defined by

$$\mathbf{f}: x \to \begin{cases} 1 & \text{for} \quad x \geqslant 0 \\ -1 & \text{for} \quad x < 0 \end{cases} \quad (x \in [-\pi, \pi]).$$

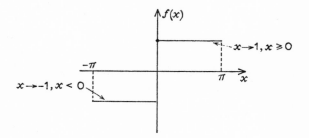

Solution

This function is an odd function, and so we can proceed to

Step 3 $\quad b_n = \dfrac{2}{\pi} \displaystyle\int_0^\pi f(x)\sin nx\, dx$

$$= \frac{2}{\pi} \int_0^\pi \sin nx\, dx$$

$$= \frac{2}{\pi} \left[-\frac{1}{n}\cos nx \right]_0^\pi$$

$$= \frac{2}{\pi} \left(-\frac{1}{n}(-1)^n + \frac{1}{n}\cdot 1 \right)$$

$$b_n = \begin{cases} \dfrac{4}{n\pi} & \text{if } n \text{ is odd} \\ 0 & \text{if } n \text{ is even.} \end{cases}$$

Thus the Fourier Series for **f** is given by

$$\mathbf{f} \simeq \frac{4}{\pi}\left\{ \sin + \frac{\sin 3}{3} + \frac{\sin 5}{5} + \dots \right\}.$$

Post-mortem

It is quite interesting to see how successful the approximation has been in this case.

Using one
term

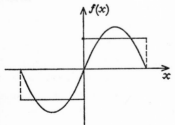

Using two
terms

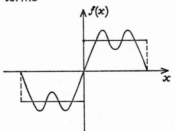

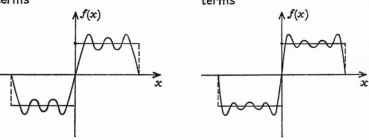

Using three terms

Using four terms

The more terms we add to the approximation, the more successful it becomes. But one point is a notable exception. The image of the point 0 under the Fourier Series is

$$\frac{4}{\pi}\left\{\sin(0)+\frac{\sin(3.0)}{3}+\frac{\sin(5.0)}{5}+...\right\}=0,$$

no matter how many terms of the approximation that we look at. Is there a problem here? The function that we started with was specified so that

$$f(0) = 1.$$

So our approximation appears to have broken down for one of the elements in the domain. And if it has broken down for one element, what is there to stop it from breaking down for more? For instance, what about an end-point of the domain?

At $x = \pi$, we get

$$\frac{4}{\pi}\left\{\sin\pi+\frac{\sin3\pi}{3}+\frac{\sin5\pi}{5}+...\right\}=0.$$

But our specified function gives

$$f(\pi) = 1.$$

Another breakdown! Will this ever stop? Well, by 'successful approximation', we clearly had in mind some sort of convergence. The next chapter examines what is meant by the convergence of a Fourier Series, and we will see that it is possible to predict with confidence where breakdowns might occur. We shall also see to what extent they affect the success of approximation.

Exercise 11

We seem to be getting into trouble with discontinuous functions. But we had similar trouble with the function of Example 1, as pointed out in the post-mortem. Are these two phenomena different?

We have been considering the vector space spanned by the functions **cos m** and **sin n**. We know that these functions are linearly independent, and that they will form a basis for some space. Because these functions are also orthogonal, it is particularly easy to calculate the coefficients of any function in this space when it is expressed in terms of the trigonometric basis. The only snag is this. Although the space is well-defined (because we know a basis for it), we have no test as to whether any function chosen at random belongs to the space. Several functions seem almost certainly to belong to the space: we have seen that their Fourier Series appear to converge to the required result very quickly, and this is what we mean when we write

'**f** = Fourier Series of **f**.'

But this last example, a discontinuous function, clearly presents problems. In the next chapter, we shall see that, even if a given function does not belong to the space, it is very often possible to find a function very 'close' to it which *does* belong to the space. That is, a function **f₁** for which we can write

'**f₁** ≃ **f**

and   **f₁** = Fourier Series of **f**.'

Summary of Chapter 3

We laid out a procedure for finding the Fourier coefficients of a function **f** with domain $[-\pi, \pi]$.

Step 1 $a_0 = \dfrac{1}{2\pi} \displaystyle\int_{-\pi}^{\pi} f(x)\,\mathrm{d}x$

Step 2 $a_m = \dfrac{1}{\pi} \displaystyle\int_{-\pi}^{\pi} f(x)\cos mx\,\mathrm{d}x$

Step 3 $b_n = \dfrac{1}{\pi} \displaystyle\int_{-\pi}^{\pi} f(x)\sin nx\,\mathrm{d}x.$

45

In order to speed the calculations, we proved

THEOREM 3.1

If **f** is an odd function, then its Fourier Series contains only functions of the type **sin n**.

We asked you to prove

THEOREM 3.2

If **f** is an even function, then its Fourier Series contains only functions of the type **cos m**.

These theorems gave rise to the idea of the Fourier Sine (and Cosine) Series of a function **f** with domain $[0, \pi]$ which can be found by extending **f** to f_1 so that f_1 is an odd (or even) function.

Finally, we showed how the general procedure given above can be adapted to cope with a function whose domain is $[a, b]$.

4 · The Success of the Approximation

*The ideas of length and distance in geometric vector spaces can be
generalised to help in the discussion of the convergence of a series of
functions. Using this generalisation, it can be shown that, in a sense,
Fourier coefficients are the best that can be chosen in a trigonometric
expansion. Our concept of Fourier Series can also be generalised in
terms of a new basis for a space of functions: the method of calculating
the coefficients remains the same and the method still gives the 'best'
choice of coefficients. It is important, however, to realise that there are
two important and essentially different ways of gauging the success
with which a series of functions approximates a given function. Both
ways have to be investigated and the Fourier Series are remarkably
successful in both senses.*

In this chapter, we shall investigate the success of a Fourier Series
approximation. First we examine just what we mean by saying that
one function approximates another. The idea of numerical approximation occurs in the discussion of, for example, iterative methods
and with convergence of sequences and series (see M.T.). The basic
mathematical ideas involved are those of limits and continuity, and
these arise in all discussions of approximation. An intuitive definition
of continuity, for instance, is

'if $f(x)$ is close to $f(a)$ for all x
close to a, then f is continuous at a.'

The intuitive idea of closeness can be expressed in a respectable
mathematical way, but, in whatever way we do it, the ideas of
distance and length are implicitly involved. How, then, can we
express ideas of distance and length when we are talking about
functions? The questions

'How long is the function **f**?'

'What is the distance between the
functions **f** and **g**?'

seem at first sight to be almost meaningless! In order to give meaning
to these questions, we shall go back to our *related problem* of

Chapter 2. Remember that we are regarding functions as vectors, elements of a vector space. Let us rephrase the questions in terms of vectors.

'How long is the vector **a**?'

'What is the distance between the vectors **a** and **b**?'

These questions certainly make sense for three-dimensional geometric vectors.

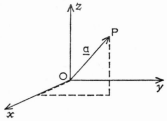

The vector **a** represents the line joining the point P to the origin, and so the length of **a** is given by

$$\text{length } (\mathbf{a}) = +\sqrt{(a_1^2 + a_2^2 + a_3^2)}$$
$$= (\mathbf{a}.\mathbf{a})^{\frac{1}{2}},$$

and the distance between vectors **a** and **b** can be thought of as being the length of the vector **a** − **b**. Thus

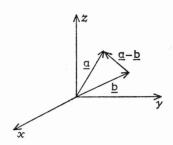

$$\text{distance between } \mathbf{a} \text{ and } \mathbf{b} = +\sqrt{[(a_1 - b_1)^2 + (a_2 - b_2)^2 + (a_3 - b_3)^2]}$$
$$= [(\mathbf{a} - \mathbf{b}).(\mathbf{a} - \mathbf{b})]^{\frac{1}{2}}.$$

Instead of the words 'distance between **a** and **b**' we use the notation:

$$\|\mathbf{a} - \mathbf{b}\|$$

which is read as '*norm* of $\mathbf{a} - \mathbf{b}$', and define, for example

$$\|\mathbf{a} - \mathbf{b}\| = [(\mathbf{a} - \mathbf{b}) \cdot (\mathbf{a} - \mathbf{b})]^{\frac{1}{2}}$$

so that

$$\text{length } (\mathbf{a}) = \|\mathbf{a} - \mathbf{0}\| = \|\mathbf{a}\|.$$

Exercise 1

Show that

(i) $\|\lambda\mathbf{a}\| = |\lambda| \, \|\mathbf{a}\| \quad (\lambda \in \mathbf{R})$.

(ii) $\|\mathbf{a}\| = 0 \Leftrightarrow \mathbf{a} = \mathbf{0}$.

Thus, we can bring the ideas of distance and length under the one umbrella by defining the distance between $\mathbf{a}$ and $\mathbf{b}$ as the length of $\mathbf{a} - \mathbf{b}$ and by interpreting length via the *scalar product*.

If we have a vector space of functions which is such that the integral

$$\int_a^b f(x)g(x)\,\mathrm{d}x$$

exists for all functions $\mathbf{f}$ and $\mathbf{g}$ in the space, then we know that we can define a scalar product by

$$\mathbf{f} \cdot \mathbf{g} = \int_a^b f(x)g(x)\,\mathrm{d}x. \qquad \text{Equation (1)}$$

Notice that we now have two spaces of functions: the space $\mathscr{S}$ of all functions for which this integral exists, and the space $\mathscr{F}$ with basis the functions $\cos m$ and $\sin n$. It is evident that all functions in $\mathscr{F}$

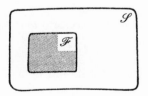

belong also to $\mathscr{S}$, and so we can perhaps hope to talk of the 'distance' between a function in $\mathscr{S}$ and its Fourier Series, which is in $\mathscr{F}$.

We can use a similar definition for length and distance in this vector space to the one we used in a geometric context, by defining the norm by the rule

$$\|\mathbf{f}\| = (\mathbf{f} \cdot \mathbf{f})^{\frac{1}{2}}.$$

This gives the answer to the first of our strange questions

'How *long* is the function **f**?'

The *length* of a function is its norm.

Exercise 2

In terms of the scalar product defined by equation (1):
  (i) give the 'distance' between two functions **f** and **g**,
  (ii) derive the results of Exercise 1,
  (iii) calculate the 'distance' between the function **f** and the function **g**, and the function **f** and the function **h**, where **f**, **g** and **h** all have domain [0, 1] and

$$\mathbf{f}: x \to x$$
$$\mathbf{g}: x \to x^2$$
$$\mathbf{h}: x \to x^3.$$

You were asked to show in Exercise 1 that

$$\|\lambda\mathbf{f}\| = |\lambda|\,\|\mathbf{f}\|.$$

This means that, as long as $\|\mathbf{f}\| \neq 0$, we can always find a vector in the 'same direction' as **f** whose length is unity. For, let

$$\mu = \|\mathbf{f}\|,$$

then $\mu \neq 0$ and

$$\left\|\frac{1}{\mu}\mathbf{f}\right\| = 1.$$

So the vector

$$\frac{\mathbf{f}}{\|\mathbf{f}\|}$$

has unit length: we call such a vector a *unit vector*. We can use this result to turn any basis

$$\{\mathbf{f}_1, \mathbf{f}_2, \mathbf{f}_3, \ldots\}$$

into a basis of unit vectors. We do this by dividing each $\mathbf{f}_i$ by $\|\mathbf{f}_i\|$ to get as a new basis the set S as follows

$$\left\{\frac{\mathbf{f}_1}{\|\mathbf{f}_1\|}, \quad \frac{\mathbf{f}_2}{\|\mathbf{f}_2\|}, \quad \frac{\mathbf{f}_3}{\|\mathbf{f}_3\|}, \quad \ldots\right\}.$$

Exercise 3

(i) Find unit vectors in the directions of the functions **f**, **g** and **h** of Exercise 2 (iii).

4 · THE SUCCESS OF THE APPROXIMATION

(ii) If the set $\{\mathbf{f}_1, \mathbf{f}_2, \mathbf{f}_3, ...\}$ is orthogonal under the definition of scalar product given above (see Equation (1)) ,and if $\mathbf{f}_i \neq \mathbf{0}$ for all i, show that the set S, defined above, is orthogonal.

Using an orthogonal set of unit vectors

$$\{\boldsymbol{\phi}_1, \boldsymbol{\phi}_2, \boldsymbol{\phi}_3, ...\}$$

as the basis for a vector space of functions, let us continue with the approach that we developed for the trigonometric functions. We express a vector $\mathbf{f}$ as a linear combination of the $\boldsymbol{\phi}_i$'s in the form

$$\mathbf{f} = a_1\boldsymbol{\phi}_1 + a_2\boldsymbol{\phi}_2 + a_3\boldsymbol{\phi}_3 + ...$$

We can find the coefficients a_i by taking the scalar product of each side of this equation with the vector $\boldsymbol{\phi}_i$.

$$\mathbf{f}.\boldsymbol{\phi}_i = a_1\boldsymbol{\phi}_1.\boldsymbol{\phi}_i + a_2\boldsymbol{\phi}_2.\boldsymbol{\phi}_i + a_3\boldsymbol{\phi}_3.\boldsymbol{\phi}_i + ...$$

This takes a particularly simple form if the $\boldsymbol{\phi}_i$'s are orthogonal and of unit length.

We then have

$$\mathbf{f}.\boldsymbol{\phi}_i = a_1 \times 0 + a_2 \times 0 + a_3 \times 0 + ... + a_i \times 1 + ...$$
$$= a_i.$$

An orthogonal basis of unit vectors is rather special and we shall, from now on, reserve the notation $\{\boldsymbol{\phi}_1, \boldsymbol{\phi}_2, ..., \boldsymbol{\phi}_n, ...\}$ for such a basis. This type of set is given a special name: an *orthonormal* set. We have seen that if $\mathbf{f}$ is in the space for which the $\boldsymbol{\phi}_i$'s form an orthonormal basis,

$$\int_a^b f(x)\phi_i(x)\mathrm{d}x = a_i,$$

and since this method for finding coefficients is so similar to the method developed for the trigonometric functions, we call the a_i's Fourier coefficients of $\mathbf{f}$ with respect to the basis $\{\boldsymbol{\phi}_i\}$. We carry the similarity further by saying that

$$\sum_{i=1}^{\infty} \left(\int_a^b f(x)\phi_i(x)\mathrm{d}x \right) \boldsymbol{\phi}_i$$

is a *Fourier Series* for $\mathbf{f}$.

It is the aim of this chapter to investigate the success with which such a Fourier Series approximates a given function. For a good

51

approximation, we will want the distance between the given function **f** and its Fourier Series to be small, that is,

$$\|\mathbf{f} - (\text{Fourier Series of } \mathbf{f})\|$$

to be small. So let us examine this distance.

If we consider the whole of the Fourier Series, then we may run into the difficulties which attend infinite series, so we restrict ourselves at first to the approximation obtained by considering only the first n terms of the series – this is standard practice when considering infinite series. Also, we shall find it easier to look at the square of the distance, since this eliminates the $\sqrt{}$ sign in the definition of the distance. We start with a very obvious fact.

$$\left\| \mathbf{f} - \sum_{i=1}^{n} a_i \phi_i \right\|^2 \geqslant 0,$$

$$\therefore \left(\mathbf{f} - \sum_{i=1}^{n} a_i \phi_i \right) \cdot \left(\mathbf{f} - \sum_{i=1}^{n} a_i \phi_i \right) \geqslant 0,$$

$$\therefore \mathbf{f} \cdot \mathbf{f} - 2\mathbf{f} \cdot \left(\sum_{i=1}^{n} a_i \phi_i \right) + \left(\sum_{i=1}^{n} a_i \phi_i \right) \cdot \left(\sum_{i=1}^{n} a_i \phi_i \right) \geqslant 0.$$

This step uses the fact that the scalar product is commutative and distributive over vector addition (see M.T.).

$$\mathbf{f} \cdot \mathbf{f} - 2 \sum_{i=1}^{n} a_i \mathbf{f} \cdot \phi_i + \left(\sum_{i,j=1}^{n} a_i a_j \phi_i \cdot \phi_j \right) \geqslant 0.$$

But, in the second term, we know that $\mathbf{f} \cdot \phi_i = a_i$ and, in the third term,

$$\phi_i \cdot \phi_j = \begin{cases} 0 & \text{if } i \neq j \\ 1 & \text{if } i = j, \end{cases}$$

so that

$$\mathbf{f} \cdot \mathbf{f} - 2 \sum_{i=1}^{n} a_i^2 + \sum_{i=1}^{n} a_i^2 \geqslant 0$$

giving

$$\boxed{\mathbf{f} \cdot \mathbf{f} \geqslant \sum_{i=1}^{n} a_i^2.}$$

Now this result is valid for all values of n, and so we can write

$$\int_a^b f^2(x)\,\mathrm{d}x \geqslant \sum_{i=1}^{\infty} a_i^2.$$

What can we deduce from this last inequality? Notice that all the elements of the series to be summed are positive. This means that the nth *partial sums*† form a sequence which is increasing with n.

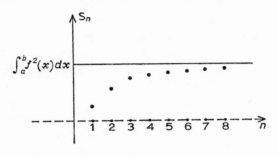

So that, as long as $\displaystyle\int_a^b f^2(x)\,dx$ exists, the terms of the summation a_i^2 must get smaller and smaller as i increases. That is

$$\lim_{i \to \infty} a_i = 0.$$

Exercise 4 (Optional)

We have only given an intuitive indication that

$$\lim_{i \to \infty} a_i = 0.$$

Prove that for any sequence $s_1, s_2, s_3, \ldots$ of positive numbers, which is such that

$$\sum_{i=1}^{\infty} s_i \leqslant K, \quad \text{some given number,}$$

then

$$\lim_{i \to \infty} s_i = 0.$$

This last result is clearly a step in the right direction. For, roughly speaking, it means that the contribution of successive terms to the final result will get smaller and smaller. But in order to obtain the result, we made an assumption.

Assumption 1 $\displaystyle\int_a^b f^2(x)\,dx$ exists.

When this is the case, we say that **f** is *square integrable*. (This assump-

---

† The nth partial sum of the series $u_1 + u_2 + u_3 + \ldots$ is $\displaystyle\sum_{i=1}^{n} u_i$.

tion is implicit in our original restriction to consider spaces of functions for which

$$\int_a^b f(x)g(x)\mathrm{d}x \text{ exists}$$

for all $\mathbf{f}$ and $\mathbf{g}$ in the space.)

The next result that we shall prove may seem rather extraordinary! So far, we have looked only at the ways in which a Fourier Series approximates a given function, and the Fourier Series is uniquely determined by the chosen basis for the vector space and by the procedure that we laid down for finding coefficients. What would happen if somebody produced a different method for finding coefficients? It is conceivable that their method might be superior, might produce a better approximation. We can prove that this is impossible in the following way.

Suppose that an alternative method for finding coefficients produced the values $c_1, c_2, c_3, \ldots$, so that the approximation was

$$\mathbf{f} = c_1\boldsymbol{\phi}_1 + c_2\boldsymbol{\phi}_2 + c_3\boldsymbol{\phi}_3 + \ldots$$

as compared with the Fourier Series of $\mathbf{f}$ with respect to $\{\boldsymbol{\phi}_i\}$ given by

$$\mathbf{f} = a_1\boldsymbol{\phi}_1 + a_2\boldsymbol{\phi}_2 + a_3\boldsymbol{\phi}_3 + \ldots.$$

Let us start by looking at the success of the new method after n terms of the series. As before, we shall simplify the algebra by looking at the square of the distance between $\mathbf{f}$ and the approximation.

$$\left\| \mathbf{f} - \sum_{i=1}^{n} c_i\phi_i \right\|^2 = \left(\mathbf{f} - \sum_{i=1}^{n} c_i\phi_i \right) \cdot \left(\mathbf{f} - \sum_{i=1}^{n} c_i\phi_i \right)$$

$$= \mathbf{f}.\mathbf{f} - 2\sum_{i=1}^{n} c_i a_i + \sum_{i=1}^{n} c_i^2$$

following the lines of the argument on page 52,

$$= \mathbf{f}.\mathbf{f} - \sum_{i=1}^{n} a_i^2 + \sum_{i=1}^{n} a_i^2 - 2\sum_{i=1}^{n} c_i a_i + \sum_{i=1}^{n} c_i^2$$

$$= \left\| \mathbf{f} - \sum_{i=1}^{n} a_i\phi_i \right\|^2 + \sum_{i=1}^{n} (a_i - c_i)^2.$$

Now unless $c_i = a_i$ for every i – in which case the new method is a bit of a cheat, since it produces exactly the same coefficients as the Fourier method – the sum

$$\sum_{i=1}^{n} (a_i - c_i)^2 > 0.$$

So we have the result:

$$\|\mathbf{f} - (c_i \text{ approximation})\|^2 \geqslant \|\mathbf{f} - (\text{Fourier approximation})\|^2.$$

This shows us that of all methods of finding coefficients, the Fourier method is the best!

A word of caution

Before our backs get sore from too much patting, it is only fair to point out that the result we have proved hinges on *our* definition of distance. We spent the first part of this chapter deciding on a reasonable definition of distance. But there are many other ways of defining distance in a vector space of functions. For one thing, our definition depends on the scalar product we chose. With a different scalar product or definition of distance, the result may not be true.

It may help you to prove some of the general results we have obtained when they are interpreted in terms of the particular basis that we discussed in the previous chapter.

Exercise 5 (Optional)

(i) If the Fourier Series of **f** is

$$\sum_{i=0}^{\infty} (a_i \cos i + b_i \sin i) \quad (b_0 = 0),$$

show that
$$\mathbf{f.f} \geqslant \sum_{i=0}^{\infty} (a_i^2 + b_i^2).$$

(ii) Show that
$$\lim_{n \to \infty} a_n = 0,$$

$$\lim_{n \to \infty} b_n = 0,$$

whenever **f** is a square integrable function over $[-\pi, \pi]$.

So far in this chapter, we have made some progress with our investigation of the success of the approximation given by Fourier Series. But we have been concerned primarily with minimizing the distance between a given function and its approximation; this amounts to 'averaging out' the square of the error as best possible. We have not, as yet, made any investigation of how the *images* of the respective functions compare. Whenever we discuss the success of an approximation we are essentially concerned with the convergence of the approximating series. So that, in terms of this chapter, if we define

$$\mathbf{f}_N = \sum_{i=1}^{N} a_i \phi_i$$

then we are interested in what happens to successive terms of the sequence $\qquad \mathbf{f}_1, \quad \mathbf{f}_2, \quad \mathbf{f}_3, \quad ..., \quad \mathbf{f}_N, \quad ....$

We first of all imagine that this sequence converges. We then want to know whether the limit of this sequence looks anything like $\mathbf{f}$. As we have just implied, this question can be interpreted in two ways. First, we can consider the distance between successive $\mathbf{f}_N$'s and $\mathbf{f}$. This corresponds to the interpretation we have been using so far. These successive distances can be measured by

$$\int_a^b (f_N(x) - f(x))^2 \, dx,$$

and if this sequence of integrals has limit zero as N tends to infinity then we say that the sequence $\{\mathbf{f}_N\}$ converges *in the mean* to $\mathbf{f}$.

A second interpretation is to consider the sequence $\{f_N(x)\}$ for a particular value of $x \in [a, b]$. If this sequence converges to a limit which is $f(x)$, then we say that $\{\mathbf{f}_N\}$ converges to $\mathbf{f}$ *pointwise at* x. The following examples show that these two types of convergence are indeed different.

Example 1

(i) Consider the sequence of functions $\{\mathbf{f}_k\}$

$$\mathbf{f}_k : x \to x^k \quad (x \in [-1, 1]).$$

This sequence converges in the mean to the zero function, because

$$\int_{-1}^{1} (f_k(x) - 0)^2 \, dx = \int_{-1}^{1} x^{2k} \, dx$$

$$= \frac{2}{2k+1}$$

$$\sim 0 \quad \text{as} \quad k \sim \infty.$$

On the other hand $\qquad f_k(-1) = (-1)^k$

and so $f_k(-1)$ oscillates between $+1$ and -1. Thus the sequence $\{f_k\}$ converges in the mean to the zero function but not pointwise at all $x \in [-1, 1]$.

(ii) Consider a sequence of spike functions $\{g_k\}$ which can be defined in terms of a formula in three parts.

$$g_k: x \to \begin{cases} k\sqrt{x} & (x \in [0, 1/k]), \\ \sqrt{(2k - k^2 x)} & (x \in [1/k, 2/k]), \\ 0 & (x \in [2/k, 1]), \end{cases}$$

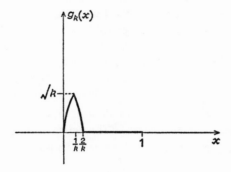

so that the domain of g_k is $[0, 1]$ for all k. For any point $\alpha \in [0, 1]$, we can find a number K for which $k > K$ implies

$$g_k(\alpha) = 0.$$

We simply have to take $K > 2/\alpha$. So the sequence $\{g_k\}$ converges to the zero function pointwise at all points $\alpha \in [0, 1]$. However $\{g_k\}$ does not converge in the mean to the zero function, since

$$\int_0^1 (g_k(x) - 0)^2 \, dx = \int_0^{1/k} k^2 x \, dx + \int_{1/k}^{2/k} (2k - k^2 x) \, dx + \int_0^1 0 \, dx$$

$$= \tfrac{1}{2} \qquad + \qquad \tfrac{1}{2} \qquad + \qquad 0$$

$$= 1$$

for all values of k.

Exercise 6 (Optional)

Show that the sequence $\{f_k\}$ where

$$\mathbf{f}_k: x \to x^{1/k} \quad (x \in [0, 1])$$

converges in the mean to the function $x \to 1$, $x \in [0, 1]$, with respect to the inner product

$$\mathbf{f} \cdot \mathbf{g} = \int_0^1 f(x) \, g(x) \, dx.$$

What can you say about the pointwise convergence of $\{\mathbf{f}_k\}$? Notice that each function $\mathbf{f}_k$ is continuous. Is this true of the pointwise limit of $\{\mathbf{f}_k\}$?

Let us now turn our attention to the central question of this chapter – 'How successful is a Fourier Series

in approximating to images?'

To discuss this question, we shall revert to the trigonometric Fourier Series. A discussion in terms of a general basis $\{\phi_i\}$ is not within the scope of this book. What we shall show is that:

(i) at every point of the interval $[-\pi, \pi]$, the Fourier Series is convergent,

(ii) the limit of the Fourier Series at each point is closely connected with the image value of the function which is being approximated.

In addition, our working will depend upon our making some assumptions about the behaviour of the function to be approximated. We have already made one such assumption on page 53,

Assumption 1 $\int_{-\pi}^{\pi} f^2(x) \, dx$ exists.

We need to make two more. You will see why we need to make these assumptions as we go through the details of the argument. For instance, they enable us to make a tangent approximation to $\mathbf{f}$ about a point $a \in [-\pi, \pi]$ of the form

$$f(x) \simeq f(a) + (x - a) \, Df(a).$$

Assumption 2

Over the interval $[-\pi, \pi]$, $\mathbf{f}$ has only a finite number of finite discontinuities.

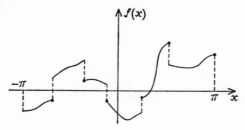

This means that we will restrict ourselves to those functions whose graphs have only a finite number of jumps – a jump being the sort of break in the graph of the function as shown in the graph above. And the jumps must be finite.

Assumption 3

At every point of the interval $[-\pi, \pi]$, the function **f** has a right-hand and a left-hand derivative.

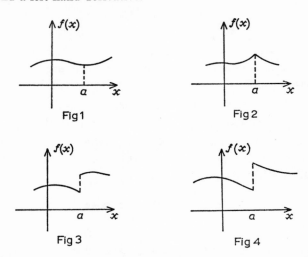

Fig 1

Fig 2

Fig 3

Fig 4

The sort of functions covered by the conditions of Assumption 3 are pictured above.

Fig. 1   At a, the function is continuous and smooth, i.e.

$$f(a_+) = f(a_-) = f(a)\dagger,$$
$$Df(a_+) = Df(a_-) = Df(a).$$

Fig. 2   At a, the function is continuous, but not smooth,

$$f(a_+) = f(a_-) = f(a),$$
$$Df(a_+) \neq Df(a_-)$$

and a is not in the domain of **Df**.

† By $f(a_-)$ we mean $\lim_{h \to 0} f(a-h)$ where h is always positive. Also $\lim_{h \to 0} f(a+h)$, where h is always positive, we denote by $f(a_+)$. In the same way $Df(a_-)$ and $Df(a_+)$ stand for left-hand and right-hand derivatives respectively – see M.T.

Fig. 3   At a, the function is neither continuous, nor smooth, i.e.

$$f(a_+) \neq f(a_-)$$

but we need $f(a)$ to exist, since f is defined on the whole of the interval $[-\pi, \pi]$, also

$$Df(a_+) \neq Df(a_-)$$

in general, and certainly $Df(a)$ does not exist.

Fig. 4   At a, the function is neither continuous nor smooth, even though

$$Df(a_+) = Df(a_-).$$

Further, although $f(a_+) \neq f(a_-)$, $f(a_+) - f(a_-)$ is a finite number.

Mathematicians have a nice term which covers the sort of functions which obey the conditions of Assumption 3. Such functions are called *piece-wise smooth*.

> 'My brother Esau is an hairy man, but I am
> a smooth man!' (presumably piece-wise).

In order to make deductions about the convergence of the Fourier approximation, at a point $a \in [-\pi, \pi]$, we look at the partial sums. We shall consider the function

$$\mathbf{f}_N = \sum_{n=0}^{N} a_n \cos n + b_n \cos n$$

and then, having found an expression for $\mathbf{f}_N$, we should be in a position to get the result we want by considering what happens to $f_N(a)$ as $N \rightsquigarrow \infty$ for any point $a \in [-\pi, \pi]$. We have

$$f_N(a) = \sum_{n=0}^{N} a_n \cos na + b_n \sin na.$$

Using the expressions for the Fourier coefficients

$$a_0, a_1, b_1, a_2, b_2, \ldots$$

which we have obtained, we get

$$
\begin{aligned}
f_N(a) = {}& \frac{1}{2\pi} \int_{-\pi}^{\pi} f(x)\,dx \\
& + \sum_{n=0}^{N} \left\{ \frac{1}{\pi} \left(\int_{-\pi}^{\pi} f(x)\cos nx\,dx \right) \cos na \right. \\
& \left. \qquad + \frac{1}{\pi} \left(\int_{-\pi}^{\pi} f(x)\sin nx\,dx \right) \sin na \right\}.
\end{aligned}
$$

Since the summation is only over a finite number of terms, we can interchange the $\int$ and the Σ. Thus

$$\pi f_N(a) = \int_{-\pi}^{\pi} f(x) \left\{ \tfrac{1}{2} + \sum_{n=0}^{N} (\cos nx \cos na + \sin nx \sin na) \right\} dx$$

$$= \int_{-\pi}^{\pi} f(x) \left\{ \tfrac{1}{2} + \sum_{n=0}^{N} \cos n(x-a) \right\} dx.$$

The problem of calculating $\tfrac{1}{2} + \sum_{n=1}^{N} \cos n(x-a)$ is the first of three problems which will arise in this investigation which we have taken out of the general discussion and collected together at the end of the chapter as Lemmas 1, 2, and 3. This one is Lemma 1 and the result of Lemma 1 is

$$\tfrac{1}{2} + \sum_{n=0}^{N} \cos n(x-a) = \frac{\sin[(N+\tfrac{1}{2})(x-a)]}{2 \sin \tfrac{1}{2}(x-a)}.$$

Thus

$$\pi f_N(a) = \int_{-\pi}^{\pi} f(x) \frac{\sin[(N+\tfrac{1}{2})(x-a)]}{2 \sin \tfrac{1}{2}(x-a)} dx.$$

We are interested in the value of this integral for a fixed a, but if we examine it closely, we see that it is just when x is close to a that the integrand needs careful consideration. This suggests that we should isolate some interval around a for special attention. We do this as follows. We write

$$\pi f_N(a) = \left(\int_{-\pi}^{a-\delta} + \int_{a-\delta}^{a+\delta} + \int_{a+\delta}^{\pi} \right) f(x) \frac{\sin[(N+\tfrac{1}{2})(x-a)]}{2 \sin \tfrac{1}{2}(x-a)} dx.$$

$$\qquad\qquad (1) \qquad\quad (2) \qquad\quad (3)$$

We are interested in what happens to $f_N(a)$ as $N \rightsquigarrow \infty$. In other words we need to know something about integrals of the form

$$\int_{\alpha}^{\beta} f(x) \frac{\sin[(N+\tfrac{1}{2})(x-a)]}{2 \sin \tfrac{1}{2}(x-a)} dx$$

as $N \rightsquigarrow \infty$. There is a standard result in analysis which we have obtained as Lemma 2 at the end of the chapter and which says that

$$\lim_{n \rightsquigarrow \infty} \int_{a}^{b} F(x) \cos nx \, dx = 0$$

and

$$\lim_{n \rightsquigarrow \infty} \int_{a}^{b} F(x) \sin nx \, dx = 0$$

61

provided F satisfies certain conditions. The first thing we do then is to get integrals (1), (2) and (3) in a suitable form for applying this result.

We shall look first at the integrals labelled (1) and (3) since they are much the same. If we use the fact that

$$\sin[(N+\tfrac{1}{2})\,(x-a)] = \sin[N(x-a)+\tfrac{1}{2}(x-a)]$$
$$= \sin\tfrac{1}{2}(x-a)\cos N(x-a)$$
$$+ \sin N(x-a)\cos\tfrac{1}{2}(x-a),$$

then

$$(1) = \int_{-\pi}^{a-\delta} f(x)\,\frac{\sin[(N+\tfrac{1}{2})\,(x-a)]}{2\sin\tfrac{1}{2}(x-a)}\,\mathrm{d}x$$

$$= \int_{-\pi}^{a-\delta} \tfrac{1}{2}f(x)\,[\cos N(x-a)+\cot\tfrac{1}{2}(x-a)\sin N(x-a)]\mathrm{d}x$$

$$= \int_{-\pi}^{a-\delta} [\tfrac{1}{2}f(x)\,(\cos Na-\cot\tfrac{1}{2}(x-a)\sin Na)]\cos Nx\,\mathrm{d}x$$

$$+ \int_{-\pi}^{a-\delta} [\tfrac{1}{2}f(x)\,(\sin Na+\cot\tfrac{1}{2}(x-a)\cos Na)]\sin Nx\,\mathrm{d}x.$$

The integrals now almost take the form of the integrals in Lemma 2, but not quite. Let us look at the part of first of them in detail.

$$\left|\int_{-\pi}^{a-\delta}\tfrac{1}{2}f(x)\cos Na\cos Nx\,\mathrm{d}x\right|$$

$$= \left|\cos Na\int_{-\pi}^{a-\delta}\tfrac{1}{2}f(x)\cos Nx\,\mathrm{d}x\right|$$

$$\leqslant \left|\int_{-\pi}^{a-\delta}\tfrac{1}{2}f(x)\cos Nx\,\mathrm{d}x\right|$$

and writing $F(x)$ for $\tfrac{1}{2}f(x)$, α for $a-\delta$ and β for $-\pi$, we have

$$\leqslant \left|\int_{\alpha}^{\beta} F(x)\cos Nx\,\mathrm{d}x\right|.$$

Lemma 2 states that as $N \leadsto \infty$, this last integral tends to zero, so we have proved that

$$\lim_{N \leadsto \infty}\int_{-\pi}^{a-\delta}\tfrac{1}{2}f(x)\cos Na\cos Nx\,\mathrm{d}x = 0.$$

Turning our attention now to the other part, we have

$$\int_{-\pi}^{a-\delta} -\tfrac{1}{2}f(x)\cot\tfrac{1}{2}(x-a)\cos Na\cos Nx\,\mathrm{d}x.$$

We can deal with it as follows. Remove the $\sin Na$ term as we removed the $\cos Na$ term above and observe that when $x \in [-\pi, a-\delta]$, $\cot\tfrac{1}{2}(x-a)$ is bounded. This is because

$$-\pi \leqslant \frac{x-a}{2} < -\frac{\delta}{2} \quad \text{when} \quad x \in [-\pi, a-\delta].$$

(The left-hand inequality is obtained by observing that x never differs from a by more than 2π.)

Thus

$$\left| \cot\left(\frac{x-a}{2}\right) \right| < \cot\left(\frac{\delta}{2}\right),$$

and since the choice of δ is independent of N, the function

$$x \to -\tfrac{1}{2}f(x)\cot\left(\frac{x-a}{2}\right) \quad (x \in [-\pi, a-\delta])$$

is bounded. Thus this integral takes the form of Lemma 2 and we have proved that

$$\lim_{N \to \infty} \int_{-\pi}^{a-\delta} \tfrac{1}{2}f(x)\cot\tfrac{1}{2}(x-a)\sin Na\cos Nx\,\mathrm{d}x = 0.$$

We can use a similar argument for the rest of (1), and this proves that

$$\lim_{N \to \infty} (1) = 0.$$

A very similar argument will yield the result

$$\lim_{N \to \infty} (3) = 0.$$

Exercise 7

Prove that

$$\lim_{N \to \infty} \left\{ \int_{a+\delta}^{\pi} f(x)\frac{\sin\left[(N+\tfrac{1}{2})(x-a)\right]}{2\sin\tfrac{1}{2}(x-a)}\,\mathrm{d}x \right\} = 0.$$

We now turn our attention to

$$(2) = \int_{a-\delta}^{a+\delta} f(x)\frac{\sin\left[(N+\tfrac{1}{2})(x-a)\right]}{2\sin\tfrac{1}{2}(x-a)}\,\mathrm{d}x.$$

We are hoping to cope with the situation when there is a jump in f at a, and so we divide (2) into two parts.

$$(2) = \left(\int_{a-\delta}^{a} + \int_{a}^{a+\delta} \right) f(x) \, \frac{\sin[(N+\frac{1}{2})\,(x-a)]}{2\sin\frac{1}{2}(x-a)} \, dx.$$

$\quad\quad\quad\quad\quad (2a) \quad\quad (2b)$

Now if δ is small enough we are justified in making the following approximations.

$\quad$ (i) $\quad\quad\quad f(x) = f(a_-) + (x-a)\,\{Df(a_-) + \epsilon(x)\}$

for $x \in (a-\delta, a)$.

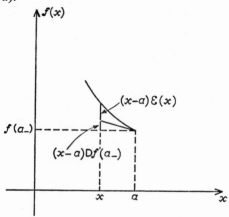

If we rearrange the equation of (i), we get

$$\frac{f(x) - f(a_-)}{(x-a)} = Df(a_-) + \epsilon(x),$$

so that $\epsilon(x)$ measures the amount that the grad derivative of f differs from $Df(a)$ when $x \in [a-\delta, a]$. If $Df(x)$ is bounded, then so is $\epsilon(x)$.

$\quad$ (ii) $\quad\quad\quad f(x) = f(a_+) + (x-a)\,\{Df(a_+) + \eta(x)\}$

for $x \in (a, a+\delta)$.

$\quad$ (iii) $\quad\quad\quad 2\sin\left(\frac{x-a}{2}\right) = x-a$

for $x \in (a-\delta, a+\delta)$.

$\quad$ (i) and (ii) are the usual tangent approximations for a function and (iii) is the approximation $\sin\theta = \theta$ for small θ.

$\quad$ As with the integrals (1) and (3), (2a) and (2b) are very similar, and so we look at one of them in detail.

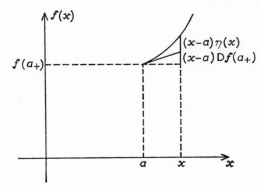

$$(2a) = \int_{a-\delta}^{a} f(x)\, \frac{\sin\left[(N+\tfrac{1}{2})\,(x-a)\right]}{2\sin\tfrac{1}{2}(x-a)}\, \mathrm{d}x$$

$$= \int_{a-\delta}^{a} f(a_-)\, \frac{\sin\left[(N+\tfrac{1}{2})\,(x-a)\right]}{x-a}\, \mathrm{d}x$$

$$+ \int_{a-\delta}^{a} \{Df(a_-) + \epsilon(x)\} \sin\left[(N+\tfrac{1}{2})(x-a)\right] \mathrm{d}x.$$

$$= f(a_-) \int_{0}^{N+\frac{1}{2}} \frac{\sin y}{y}\, \mathrm{d}y,$$

where we have used a change of variable

$$(N+\tfrac{1}{2})\,(x-a) = -y$$

and have taken the constant $f(a_-)$ outside the integral. We have set up this integral so that it takes the form of the integral in Lemma 3

$$\int_{0}^{\infty} \frac{\sin x}{x}\, \mathrm{d}x = \tfrac{1}{2}\pi$$

(see page 73) ready to let $N \rightsquigarrow \infty$.

$$= \int_{-\delta}^{0} F_1(y)\cos Ny\, \mathrm{d}y$$

$$+ \int_{-\delta}^{0} F_2(y)\sin Ny\, \mathrm{d}y,$$

where we have first written

$$\sin\left[(N+\tfrac{1}{2})\,(x-a)\right]$$
$$= \sin N(x-a)\cos\tfrac{1}{2}(x-a)$$
$$+ \cos N(x-a)\sin\tfrac{1}{2}(x-a)$$

and then used a change of variable

$$(x-a) = y$$

and defined functions F_1 and F_2 by the rules
$$F_1(y) = \{Df(a_-) + \epsilon(y+a)\}\sin\tfrac{1}{2}y$$
$$F_2(y) = \{Df(a_-) + \epsilon(y+a)\}\cos\tfrac{1}{2}y.$$

If we now let $N \sim \infty$, and use the results of Lemmas 2 and 3,

$$\lim_{N \sim \infty} (2a) = f(a_-) \times \tfrac{1}{2}\pi + (0+0).$$

A very similar argument will yield the result

$$\lim_{N \sim \infty} (2b) = f(a_+) \times \tfrac{1}{2}\pi.$$

Exercise 8

Prove that

$$\lim_{N \to \infty} \left\{ \int_a^{a+\delta} f(x)\, \frac{\sin\left[(N+\tfrac{1}{2})\,(x-a)\right]}{2 \sin \tfrac{1}{2}(x-a)}\, \mathrm{d}x \right\} = \tfrac{1}{2}\pi f(a_+).$$

Now that we have dealt with (2), let us collect together all the results that we have proved

$$\lim_{N \sim \infty} \pi f_N(a) = \lim_{N \sim \infty} (1) + \lim_{N \sim \infty} (2) + \lim_{N \sim \infty} (3)$$

$$= 0 + f(a_-) \times \tfrac{1}{2}\pi + f(a_+) \times \tfrac{1}{2}\pi + 0.$$

Thus
$$\lim_{N \sim \infty} f_N(a) = \frac{f(a_-) + f(a_+)}{2}.$$

Finally, if we collect together the various assumptions that we have made in developing this result, including those made in proving the lemmas we have the following theorem.

THEOREM 4.1

If the function f with domain $[-\pi,\ \pi]$

    (i)   is square-integrable,

    (ii) contains only a finite number of finite discontinuities (see Lemma 2),

    (iii) is piece-wise smooth,

    (iv) is bounded, with bounded derived function DF (see also Lemma 2), then the Fourier Series of **f** is convergent at every point $a \in [-\pi,\ \pi]$ and it converges to the limit

$$\frac{f(a_-) + f(a_+)}{2}.$$

4 · THE SUCCESS OF THE APPROXIMATION

Exercise 9

In order to consolidate your understanding of Theorem 4.1, we suggest that you write out the proof for yourself using the following flow chart to guide you towards the main steps of the argument.

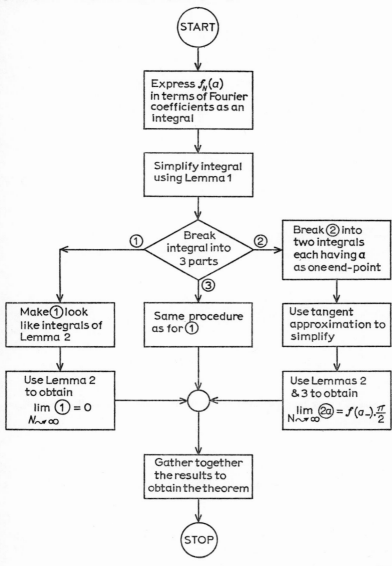

FOURIER SERIES

Post-mortem

(i)

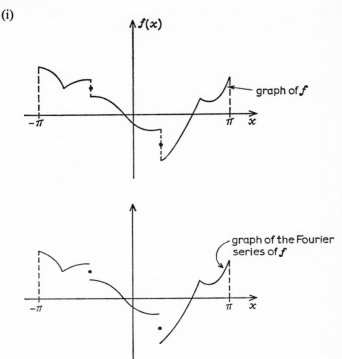

We have already said that if **f** is continuous at a, then

$$f(a_-) = f(a_+) = f(a).$$

Thus at every point of continuity of the function **f**, its Fourier Series converges to

$$\frac{f(a_-) + f(a_+)}{2} = f(a).$$

So that at points of continuity, the Fourier Series gives the right result. At points of discontinuity, the Fourier Series settles for a point which is half way between $f(a_-)$ and $f(a_+)$. What could be fairer! It does mean however that, if a is a point of discontinuity of **f**, then we have no guarantee that the Fourier Series gives the 'right' result (i.e. $f(a)$); in general, it does not (see Example 4, Chapter 3).

(ii) In Chapter 3, we saw how we could extend the domain of a function **f** defined on $[-\pi, \pi]$ so that the Fourier Series approximates to **f** for all values of x. The method of defining **f** was to make it a periodic function, with period 2π. The results of the theorem still apply to this extended function.

We can also apply the results to the case where **f** is defined on the general interval $[a, b]$. This general extension of the results gives us a very broad range of functions for which we can safely apply Fourier Series.

(iii) We have shown that given any point $a \in [-\pi, \pi]$, then the Fourier Series converges to $f(a)$ provided

$$f(x) = \tfrac{1}{2}[f(x_+) + f(x_-)]$$

for all $x \in [-\pi, \pi]$. In the next chapter, we shall see how the Fourier Series behaves near a point of discontinuity. This behaviour is known as Gibb's Phenomenon.

(iv) Finally, concerning the assumptions that we have made, they are by no means a minimum set. Indeed, Fourier Series are such remarkable things that, even if the Fourier Series for a function **f** does not converge, it is often possible to recover values of $f(x)$ from the series! Of course, the way in which one thinks of summing a series has to be bent a little, but that is all part of the fun (see Titchmarsh, *Theory of Functions* (Oxford)). The investigation of convergence and summation of Fourier Series is, in fact, still a current research problem.

For the rest of this chapter, we shall concern outselves with proving the lemmas that we assumed for the proof of Theorem 4.1. We have included these proofs, not only for the sake of tidying up the loose ends, but also because they are each good examples of standard procedures of getting results in analysis.

LEMMA 1

$$\tfrac{1}{2} + \sum_{n=1}^{N} \cos n(x-a) = \frac{\sin[(N+\tfrac{1}{2})(x-a)]}{2\sin\tfrac{1}{2}(x-a)}.$$

Proof

The general approach to this kind of summation is the following. To find

$$\sum_{n=1}^{N} \cos n\theta$$

69

let
$$C = \sum_{n=1}^{N} \cos n\theta,$$

$$S = \sum_{n=1}^{N} \sin n\theta,$$

obtain an expression for $C+iS$ and then equate real and imaginary parts.

If we put $(x-a) = \theta$, then we can use this approach to prove the lemma.

$$\tfrac{1}{2} + \sum_{n=1}^{N} \cos n\theta + i \sum_{n=1}^{N} \sin n\theta \tag{1}$$

$$= \tfrac{1}{2} + \sum_{n=1}^{N} (\cos n\theta + i \sin n\theta)$$

$$= \tfrac{1}{2} + \sum_{n=1}^{N} e^{in\theta}$$

$$= \tfrac{1}{2} + e^{i\theta} \left(\frac{1 - e^{iN\theta}}{1 - e^{i\theta}} \right)$$

using the formula for the sum of a geometric progression.

To find the real and imaginary parts of this sort of expression, we would normally try to make the denominator of the fraction into a real number. We know that

$$\sin x = \frac{1}{2i} (e^{ix} - e^{-ix}),$$

so we adapt the expression so that it becomes

$$= \tfrac{1}{2} + \frac{e^{i\theta/2} - e^{i(N+\frac{1}{2})\theta}}{e^{-i\theta/2} - e^{i\theta/2}}$$

$$= \frac{(e^{-i\theta/2} + e^{i\theta/2}) - 2e^{i(N+\frac{1}{2})\theta}}{-4i \sin (\tfrac{1}{2}\theta)}$$

$$= \frac{\sin (N+\tfrac{1}{2})\theta}{2 \sin (\tfrac{1}{2}\theta)} + i \left(\frac{\cos (\tfrac{1}{2}\theta) - \cos (N+\tfrac{1}{2})\theta}{2 \sin (\tfrac{1}{2}\theta)} \right). \tag{2}$$

Putting $(x-a) = \theta$ and equating the real parts of lines (1) and (2) gives the required result.

LEMMA 2

$$\lim_{n \to \infty} \int_a^b F(x) \cos nx \, dx = 0,$$

$$\lim_{n \to \infty} \int_a^b F(x) \sin nx \, dx = 0.$$

Proof

The way we shall approach these integrals is to integrate by parts. In this process, we shall want to differentiate F. Now we have already seen that we often want to find the Fourier Series of a function which is not differentiable throughout its domain, so it is rather restrictive to assume that F should be differentiable throughout $[a, b]$. Instead, let us suppose that we can divide up the interval $[a, b]$ into m sub-intervals in such a way that F is continuous and differentiable on each such sub-interval. Let us denote the end-points of the intervals by $a_0, a_1, a_2, ..., a_m$, where $a = a_0 < a_1 < a_2 < ... < a_{m-1} < a_m = b$. Then

$$\int_a^b F(x) \cos nx \, dx = \int_{a_0}^{a_1} F(x) \cos nx \, dx$$

$$+ \int_{a_1}^{a_2} F(x) \cos nx \, dx + ... + \int_{a_{m-1}}^{a_m} F(x) \cos nx \, dx.$$

Let us look at one of these integrals in isolation and integrate by parts

$$\int_{a_{r-1}}^{a_r} F(x) \cos nx \, dx$$

$$= \left[\frac{1}{n} F(x) \sin nx \right]_{a_{r-1}}^{a_r} - \int_{a_{r-1}}^{a_r} \frac{1}{n} DF(x) \sin nx \, dx$$

$$= \frac{1}{n} \left\{ F(a_r) \sin (na_r) - F(a_{r-1}) \sin (na_{r-1}) - \int_{a_{r-1}}^{a_r} DF(x) \sin nx \, dx \right\}.$$

Thus, taking the modulus of each side and using the fact that for any real numbers α, β,

$$|\alpha + \beta| \le |\alpha| + |\beta|,$$

71

we see that

$$\left| \int_{a_{r-1}}^{a} F(x)\cos nx\,\mathrm{d}x \right|$$

$$\leqslant \frac{1}{n}\left\{ |F(a_r)\sin na_r| + |F(a_{r-1})\sin na_{r-1}| + \left| \int_{a_{r-1}}^{a_r} \mathrm{D}F(x)\sin nx\,\mathrm{d}x \right| \right\}$$

$$\leqslant \frac{1}{n}\{|F(a_r)| + |F(a_{r-1})| + K(a_r - a_{r-1})\},$$

where K is the maximum value of $|\mathrm{D}F(x)|$ for $x \in [a_{r-1}, a_r]$, so that

$$|\mathrm{D}F(x)\sin(nx)| \leqslant K.$$

Thus, if M is the maximum value of $|F(x)|$ for $x \in [a, b]$,

$$\left| \int_{a_{r-1}}^{a_r} F(x)\cos nx\,\mathrm{d}x \right| \leqslant \frac{1}{n}\{2M + (a_r - a_{r-1})K\}.$$

[Notice that we have made another assumption here; that both M and K exist, i.e. that $F(x)$ and $\mathrm{D}F(x)$ are both bounded throughout $[a, b]$.] Thus

$$\left| \int_{a}^{b} F(x)\cos nx\,\mathrm{d}x \right|$$

$$\leqslant \left| \int_{a_0}^{a_1} F(x)\cos nx\,\mathrm{d}x \right| + \ldots + \left| \int_{a_{m-1}}^{b} F(x)\cos nx\,\mathrm{d}x \right|$$

$$\leqslant \frac{1}{n}\{2Mm + (b-a)K\}.$$

Since a, b, M, m, and K are finite, fixed and independent of n, this inequality shows us that as n gets larger and larger,

$$\left| \int_{a}^{b} F(x)\cos nx\,\mathrm{d}x \right|$$

gets smaller and smaller. To put it formally,

$$\lim_{n \to 0} \int_{a}^{b} F(x)\cos nx\,\mathrm{d}x = 0.$$

The second part of the lemma,

$$\lim_{x \to 0} \int_{a}^{b} F(x)\sin nx\,\mathrm{d}x = 0$$

can be proved in a similar way.

4 · THE SUCCESS OF THE APPROXIMATION

Post-mortem

(i) If we put $a = -\pi$, $b = \pi$, then the integrals are just the Fourier coefficients a_n and b_n. We have proved, in the result of the lemma, that for this case

$$\lim_{n \to 0} a_n = \lim_{n \to 0} b_n = 0$$

a result that you proved in general in Exercise 5. You may wonder, then, what we are worrying about if we have proved these results before. But we had not. It is simply the presence of more general limits of integration that force us to provide a new proof. For while

$$\text{Lemma 2} \Rightarrow \text{Exercise 5,}$$

Exercise 6 being a special case of Lemma 2, we are not justified in reversing the implication.

(ii) Are the results of Lemma 2 surprising? We think not, for the graph of the function $\mathbf{F} \times \cos \mathbf{n}$ is as follows

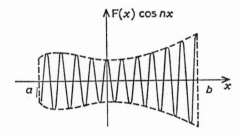

(it is no sooner up, than it is down again!). Thus when we come to integrate, there will be almost as much positive as negative area. Intuitively it seems likely that the integral tends to zero as n increases.

LEMMA 3
$$\int_0^\infty \frac{\sin x}{x} \, dx = \frac{\pi}{2}.$$

Proof

It is the x underneath in the integrand that gives trouble here, so we use the following device to get rid of it. Let $\mathbf{F}$ be the function with domain $\mathbf{R}_0^+$ such that

$$F(t) = \int_0^\infty e^{-tx} \frac{\sin x}{x} \, dx \quad (t \in \mathbf{R}_0^+)$$

then the integral we are looking for is $F(0)$.

73

The point of this device is that if we differentiate **F**, then the term e^{-tx} will produce an x in the numerator to cancel with the x in the denominator which was causing us trouble. Thus, assuming that we are allowed to perform this differentiation, we have

$$\mathrm{D}F(t) = \int_0^\infty -e^{-tx}\sin x\,\mathrm{d}x$$

$$= [-e^{-tx}\cos x]_0^\infty + \int_0^\infty te^{-tx}\cos x\,\mathrm{d}x$$

$$= -1 + t\int_0^\infty e^{-tx}\cos x\,\mathrm{d}x$$

$$= -1 + t[e^{-tx}\sin x]_0^\infty - t\int_0^\infty -te^{-tx}\sin x\,\mathrm{d}x$$

$$= -1 + t\times 0 - t^2\mathrm{D}F(t).$$

So that
$$\mathrm{D}F(t) = \frac{-1}{1+t^2}$$

giving
$$F(t) = -\arctan t + c,$$

where c is a constant. Thus,

$$F(0) = -\arctan 0 + c$$

and so
$$F(0) = c.$$

Since $F(0)$ is the integral we seek, we are looking for the value of c. It seems intuitively clear that as $t \leadsto \infty$,

$$\left(\int_0^\infty e^{-tx}\frac{\sin x}{x}\,\mathrm{d}x\right) \leadsto \int_0^\infty 0\,\mathrm{d}x = 0.$$

So that, arguing on this intuitive level, as $t \leadsto \infty$, since $\arctan t \leadsto \dfrac{\pi}{2}$, we have

$$0 = -\frac{\pi}{2} + c,$$

$$c = \frac{\pi}{2}.$$

This gives us the result that we need;

$$\int_0^\infty \frac{\sin x}{x}\,\mathrm{d}x = \frac{\pi}{2}.$$

Another way of showing that $c = \dfrac{\pi}{2}$ is as follows. It is a standard result that

$$\left|\frac{\sin x}{x}\right| \leqslant 1 \quad \text{for} \quad x \in [0, \infty).$$

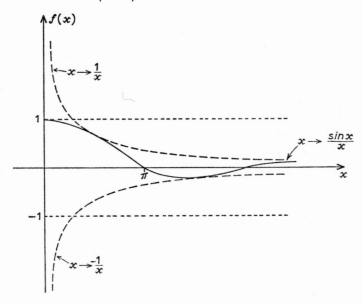

Since e^{-tx} is positive when $x \in [0, \infty)$

$$\left| e^{-tx}\, \frac{\sin x}{x}\right| \leqslant e^{-tx}$$

and $$\left| \int_0^\infty e^{-tx}\, \frac{\sin x}{x}\, dx \right| \leqslant \int_0^\infty e^{-tx}\, dx.$$

We can evaluate the last integral because

$$\int_0^N e^{-tx}\, dx = \left[-\frac{1}{t}\, e^{-tx} \right]_0^N$$

$$= \frac{1}{t}\, (1 - e^{-tN})$$

and as $N \sim \infty$, $e^{-tN} \sim 0$, so that

$$\int_0^\infty e^{-tx}\, dx = \frac{1}{t}$$

75

and we conclude that

$$\left| \int_0^\infty x \mapsto e^{-tx} \frac{\sin x}{x} \, dx \right| \leqslant \frac{1}{t}.$$

Now letting $t \leadsto \infty$ in this inequality we obtain the result

$$\lim_{t \leadsto \infty} F(t) = 0.$$

We can then proceed as above to show that the constant $= \dfrac{\pi}{2}$.

Summary of Chapter 4

In this chapter, we have investigated the distance between a function and its Fourier Series, having defined distance in terms of a norm,

$$\|\mathbf{f} - \mathbf{g}\| = \left\{ \int_a^b (f(x) - g(x))^2 \, dx \right\}^{\frac{1}{2}}.$$

For a general space of functions, in which

$$\mathbf{f} = \sum_{i=1}^\infty \left(\int_a^b f(x) \phi_i(x) \, dx \right) \boldsymbol{\phi}_i = \sum_{i=1}^\infty a_i \boldsymbol{\phi}_i$$

we showed that $\qquad \mathbf{f}.\mathbf{f} \geqslant \sum a_i^2$

and went on to indicate that, of all approximations, the Fourier Series is the best, that is, in the sense that

$$\left\| \mathbf{f} - \sum_{i=1}^\infty c_i \boldsymbol{\phi}_i \right\| \geqslant \left\| \mathbf{f} - \sum_{i=1}^\infty a_i \boldsymbol{\phi}_i \right\|.$$

These early remarks concerned the convergence in the mean of a Fourier Series. The rest of the chapter was devoted to the pointwise convergence of a Fourier Series. We proved

THEOREM 4.1

If the function $\mathbf{f}$, with domain $[-\pi, \pi]$ is
   (i)   is square-integrable,
   (ii) contains only a finite number of discontinuities,
   (iii) is piece-wise smooth,
   (iv) is bounded, with bounded derived function $\mathbf{Df}$,

then the Fourier Series of **f** is convergent at every point $a \in [-\pi, \pi]$ and it converges to the limit

$$\frac{f(a_-) + f(a_+)}{2}.$$

To prove this theorem, we used the following lemmas.

LEMMA 1 $\qquad 1 + \sum_{n=1}^{N} \cos n(x-a) = \dfrac{\sin[(N+\frac{1}{2})(x-a)]}{2\sin\frac{1}{2}(x-a)}.$

LEMMA 2 $\qquad\qquad \lim_{n \to \infty} \int_{a}^{b} F(x)\cos nx\,dx = 0,$

$$\lim_{n \to \infty} \int_{a}^{b} F(x)\sin nx\,dx = 0.$$

LEMMA 3 $\qquad\qquad \int_{0}^{\infty} \dfrac{\sin x}{x}\,dx = \dfrac{\pi}{2}.$

5 · Case Studies

So far, Fourier Series have been presented as a method of approximating to a given function. Along the way, examples and exercises have shown how this can be done. But all the functions which we were approximating had perfectly adequate expressions in terms other than the basis vectors

$$\mathbf{1, \cos, \sin, \cos 2, \sin 2, \ldots}$$

Even functions which have to be expressed algebraically in parts, such as

$$f\colon x \to \begin{cases} 1 & \text{for} \quad x \geqslant 0 \\[2mm] -1 & \text{for} \quad x < 0 \end{cases} \qquad (x \in [-\pi, \pi])$$

are very much simpler than the one expression

$$\mathbf{f} = \frac{4}{\pi}\left\{\sin + \frac{\sin 3}{3} + \frac{\sin 5}{5} + \ldots\right\}$$

for example, which is its trigonometric Fourier Series. You might think that you have been lead up a gum tree – stuck in a world of complicated **cos m** and **sin n** approximations with no particular way to go.

But one very important area where Fourier Series are used is in the solution of differential equations. There, when one has no neat formula for the solution, one can often find approximations to the solution. One such type of approximation is actually to calculate approximate numerical values for $f(x)$, where **f** is the solution, and to use these to build up a picture for **f**. Another method is to find a formula which approximates to $f(x)$ over some given range. For example, one might be able to use the differential equation to find a Taylor expansion for $f(x)$ (see M.T.). A Taylor expansion is essentially an approximation using polynomials, and we have now seen that this is by no means the only possibility for approximation.

78

Whenever we have an orthogonal basis we have the possibility of a Fourier-type approximation.

In this chapter, we shall look at ways in which we can use Fourier Series to solve problems. We have presented the material in a series of case studies. Each study is reasonably self-contained and so you can pick and choose which you read. However, Case Study 3 contains important ideas which are discussed in full, and so you would be well advised to read that one if no other.

You will appreciate that this is not a book on differential equations, and so the treatments we offer are rather sketchy. On the other hand, we have tried to put in enough detail to show you the sort of mathematics that is involved in each case.

Case Study 1 **Oscillations**

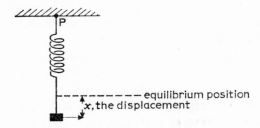

A mass M suspended by a spring from a fixed point P will hang in equilibrium unless it is disturbed. When it is disturbed, we can describe the resulting motion by using the function **f** whose domain is an interval of time, where

f: $t \to x$, the displacement from the

equilibrium position ($t \in R_0^+$)

and where **f** obeys the simple harmonic motion equation

$$D^2\mathbf{f} + \omega^2\mathbf{f} = 0.$$

$$\left[\text{Here, } \omega^2 = \frac{\lambda}{Mg}, \text{ where } \lambda \text{ is the modulus of elasticity of the spring.} \right]$$

We want to consider the situation where the end of the spring is no longer kept fixed. If the end P is jerked up and down, then the mathematical approximation is that P moves like a 'step function' of period $2T$, say, as described by the function **g** with the following graph.

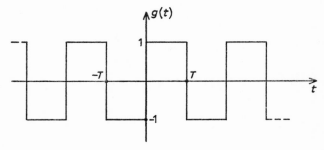

With this added complication, the equation of motion becomes

$$D^2\mathbf{f} + \omega^2\mathbf{f} = \mathbf{g}.$$

Since **g** is periodic, it is not surprising that we find that the best way of proceeding is to express **g** in terms of its Fourier Series at the point t;

$$g(t) = \frac{\pi}{4}\left\{\sin\left(\frac{\pi}{T}t\right) + \tfrac{1}{3}\sin\left(\frac{3\pi}{T}t\right) + \tfrac{1}{5}\sin\left(\frac{5\pi}{T}t\right) + \dots\right\},$$

see Example 4, page 42. Now we know that the complementary function part of the solution of the equation of motion is f_1, where

$$f_1(t) = A\cos\omega t + B\sin\omega t$$

(see M.T.). We want to find the particular integral.

The particular solution will be the sum of the particular integrals for each of the terms in the Fourier Series for **g**. A typical term in this series is

$$\frac{1}{2n+1}\sin\frac{(2n+1)\pi t}{T}.$$

We can use the standard technique for finding particular integrals corresponding to this sort of expression (see M.T.) to get the particular integral

$$\frac{\sin\left(\dfrac{(2n+1)\pi t}{T^2}\right)}{(2n+1)\left\{\omega^2 - \dfrac{(2n+1)^2\pi^2}{T^2}\right\}}.$$

The general solution is obtained by adding each of these parts of the particular solution to the complementary function.

$$f(t) = A\cos\omega t + B\sin\omega t + \frac{4}{\pi}\sum_{n=0}^{\infty}\frac{\sin\left(\dfrac{(2n+1)\pi t}{T}\right)}{(2n+1)\left\{\omega^2 - \dfrac{(2n+1)^2\pi^2}{T^2}\right\}}.$$

Suppose now that we know how the system is set up to start with. These starting conditions are sometimes called *boundary conditions*. We shall look at the simplest of cases, namely when everthing starts at rest and in equilibrium. This situation is specified by the boundary conditions

$$f(0) = 0,$$

$$Df(0) = 0.$$

The only unknowns in the expression for **f** are the numbers A and B.

The first of these conditions gives us the result

$$A = 0.$$

The second gives us the result

$$\omega B + \frac{4}{\pi} \sum_{n=0}^{\infty} \frac{\pi T}{\omega^2 T^2 - (2n+1)^2 \pi^2} = 0,$$

$$B = -\frac{4}{\omega} \sum_{n=0}^{\infty} \frac{T}{\omega^2 T^2 - (2n+1)^2 \pi^2}.$$

Thus the problem is completely solved. Notice that we are in trouble over the summation if for any n,

$$\omega^2 T^2 - (2n+1)^2 \pi^2 = 0,$$

i.e. $$2T = 2\pi,$$

where $2T$ is the period of the pushing force. If $2T$ does take one of these values, the mathematics predicts infinite displacement; then we have resonance and the system breaks up.

The reason why it was useful to use Fourier Series in this problem was because we have a known technique for finding the particular integral for an equation of the type

$$D^2 f(x) + \omega^2 f(x) = g(x)$$

where **g** is function involving sines or cosines. But if **g** is a function of the type that we started with, for which we have no standard technique available, then it is more conveniently expressed as a Fourier Series. You may have noticed that we have made no mention of the affect on the convergence of the series when we differentiate or integrate each term. For instance we assumed that differentiating the series term by term would not affect its convergence in order to find the value of B. An investigation of conditions under which such a process gives sensible results is one of the ways in which the subject of Fourier Series can be developed (see Titchmarsh, *Theory of Functions* (Oxford)).

Case Study 2   Gibbs Phenomenon†

The American physicist Albert Michelson is noted for his work on instruments of extraordinary precision. It was he who persuaded the U.S. Coastal and Geodetic Survey to measure the distance between points on Mounts Wilson and San Antonio – about 22 miles – to an accuracy of within 2 inches. At the time he was trying to measure the speed of light. Earlier, he had been interested in investigating the accuracy of Fourier Series. In 1898, he developed a harmonic analyser by which he could add up the first 80 terms of a Fourier Series. The accuracy of the approximation for a continuous function is remarkable. But for a discontinuous function, the result which Michelson got, led him to believe that there were discrepancies which had not been adequately explained. He tried adding up the terms of the Fourier Series of the step function which we met in Example 4 of Chapter 3.

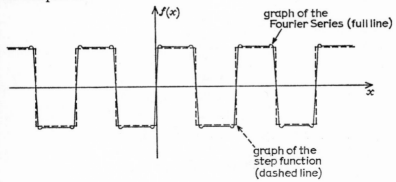

It looked to Michelson as though the Fourier Series overshot the values ± 1 at either end of the step, although the approximation in the middle of the step was still very good. He asked Josiah Gibbs to investigate this discrepancy from the mathematical point of view and it has come to be known as Gibbs Phenomenon. Let us look at the mathematical point of view. We shall take one particular point where

† This case study is rather different – it is not an example of how Fourier Series are used to solve a problem, rather it is a discussion of a trouble which can occur when using Fourier Series.

the over-shooting occuts, on the positive side of the origin. We start by making a finite Fourier Series approximation to **f**.

$$f_N(x) = \frac{4}{\pi}\left\{\sin x + \frac{\sin 3x}{3} + \ldots + \frac{\sin(2N-1)x}{2N-1}\right\}.$$

From the graph, it looks as though the maximum overshoot occurs when the graph of f_N has its first turning point, that is, the first positive x for which

$$Df_N(x) = 0.$$

Now $$Df_N(x) = \frac{4}{\pi}\{\cos x + \cos 3x + \ldots + \cos(2N-1)x\},$$

and we have a general method for finding the value of this sort of summation (see Lemma 1 of Chapter 4). Let

$$C = \cos x + \cos 3x + \ldots + \cos(2N-1)x,$$
$$S = \sin x + \sin 3x + \ldots + \sin(2N-1)x.$$

Then $$C + iS = e^{ix}\{1 + e^{2ix} + \ldots + e^{2(N-1)ix}\}$$

$$= e^{ix}\frac{1 - e^{2Nix}}{1 - e^{2ix}}$$

$$= \tfrac{1}{2}i\frac{(1 - e^{2Nix})}{\sin x},$$

and so $$C + iS = \frac{\sin 2Nx}{2\sin x} + i\frac{1 - \cos 2Nx}{2\sin x}.$$

Equating the real parts of this equation gives

$$Df_N(x) = \frac{2}{\pi}\frac{\sin 2Nx}{\sin x}.$$

Thus $Df_N(x) = 0$ for the first time when

$$x = \frac{\pi}{2N}.$$

We could find the value of f_N at this peak and then let $N \sim \infty$, but there is an easier way of looking at things. For

$$Df_N(x) = \frac{2}{\pi}\frac{\sin 2Nx}{\sin x}$$

and so $$f_N(x) = \int_0^x \frac{2}{\pi}\frac{\sin 2N\theta}{\sin \theta}\,d\theta.$$

We choose the lower limit as 0 because we know that $f_N(0) = 0$. We therefore have

$$f_N\left(\frac{\pi}{2N}\right) = \frac{2}{\pi}\int_0^{\pi/2N}\frac{\sin 2N\theta}{\sin\theta}\,d\theta$$

$$= \frac{2}{\pi}\int_0^{\pi}\frac{\sin\phi}{2N\sin\left(\dfrac{\phi}{2N}\right)}\,d\phi.$$

If we let N get large, then in the range $[0, \pi]$, we can approximate $\sin\left(\dfrac{\phi}{2N}\right)$ by $\dfrac{\phi}{2N}$ to give

$$f_N\left(\frac{\pi}{2N}\right) \simeq \frac{2}{\pi}\int_0^{\pi}\frac{\sin\phi}{\phi}\,d\phi.$$

This integral is rather like the one we had for Lemma 2 of Chapter 4.

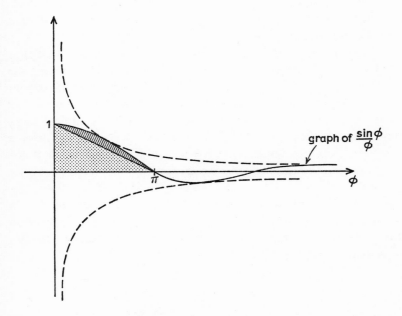

graph of $\dfrac{\sin\phi}{\phi}$

Notice that the integral is made up of two parts, as shown in the following diagram.

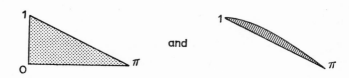

The area of the triangle is $\frac{1}{2}\pi$, so that

$$f_N\left(\frac{\pi}{2N}\right) = 1 + \frac{2}{\pi} \times (\text{area of the curved shape})$$

which is strictly greater than one. This shows that the Fourier Series does in fact over-shoot. The natural outcome of this demonstration is to ask where Theorem 4.1 stands in relation to this result – for it seems that we have a contradiction. In fact we have not, for remember that we only proved the theorem for a fixed point a. Thus, even if we choose a very close to 0, we find that by making N large enough, we can make $\frac{\pi}{2N}$ so small that the over-shooting takes place between a and 0 and that by the time a is reached, the Fourier Series will have settled down again to being very close to 1.

What we have demonstrated, however, is this. Suppose that f_N is the approximation to a function **f** which is obtained by taking the first N terms of its Fourier Series. Then although one can always find N large enough to make $|f_N(x) - f(x)|$ as small as we please for for *any* given x in an interval where the function is continuous and smooth, it is not possible to choose such an N for which this error is less than any given small quantity for *all* x when f has jump discontinuities. (Essentially, what we are saying is that if **f** is piece-wise smooth over a closed interval, then its Fourier Series converges *uniformly* to $f(x)$ on that interval. But this is not the case for an interval with a jump discontinuity. For a discussion of uniform convergence see, for example, Whittaker and Watson, *Modern Analysis* (Cambridge).)

> *The Ostrich is a silly bird*
> *With scarcely any mind*
> *He often runs so very fast*
> *He leaves himself behind.*
>
> Mary E. Wilkins Freeman

Case Study 3   The Wave Equation

The study of Fourier Series really began with the problems involved in solving the wave equation. In 1775, D. Bernoulli suggested the method of 'separating the variables' that we shall follow, but, unfortunately, the processes of analysis were not sufficiently advanced for Bernoulli to prove that his solution, which entails the expansion of a function by its Fourier Series, was actually valid. The problem for him lay in the fact that he could not show, as we have done in Theorem 4.1, that it is not necessary to demand that a function be infinitely differentiable before its Fourier Series converges. The general belief was that since the **cos m** and **sin n** functions are so delightfully smooth, any combination of them would be equally smooth. Joseph Fourier presented a paper to the French Academy in 1805 in which he showed that what we now call Fourier Series need not be restricted to differentiable functions, and later in the 19th century Dirichlet set up a very general set of criteria for functions to be representable by Fourier Series. Very recently, these criteria have been further refined. Bernoulli's problem has its origin in the particular wave equation that models the motion of a vibrating string.

To derive the equation we look for a function which tells us the shape of the string at any moment of time after it has been set vibrating. That is, we need a function ϕ such that

$$\phi : (x, t) \rightarrow \phi(x, t),$$

where $x \in [0, l]$, l being the length of the string, $t \in R_0^+$ and $\phi(x, t)$ is the displacement at a distance x from one end of the string at time t.

We can find an equation of motion by considering the forces which act on a small element of the string at time t.

87

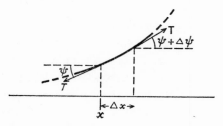

We have to make two assumptions:
    (i) the tension T in the string remains constant,
    (ii) the string only vibrates up and down (not laterally).

Then, if ρ is the mass per unit length of the string and using D_t to denote differentiation with respect to t, then Newton's Law of motion can be applied to give

$$
\begin{aligned}
\text{Mass} \times \text{Acceleration} \;&=\; \text{Force} \\
\rho \Delta s \; D_t^2 \phi(x, t) \;&=\; T\sin(\psi + \Delta\psi) - T\sin\psi \\
&=\; T\{\sin\psi \cos\Delta\psi + \cos\psi \sin\Delta\psi - \sin\psi\}.
\end{aligned}
$$

If we make the approximations that

$$\cos\Delta\psi = 1,$$
$$\sin\Delta\psi = \Delta\psi,$$

we get
$$\rho\Delta s D_t^2 \phi(x, t) = T\Delta\psi\cos\psi.$$

We now have the problem of dealing with Δs and $\Delta\psi$. This can be done in an intuitive way using the approximate diagram obtained

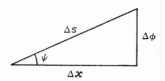

by assuming the small section of string to be straight. We then see that
$$\tan\psi = D_x\phi(x, t),$$
and if we differentiate with respect to x, we get

$$\sec^2\psi \, \frac{\Delta\psi}{\Delta x} = D_x^2 \phi(x, t).$$

Now, since
$$\frac{\Delta\psi}{\Delta s} = \frac{\Delta\psi}{\Delta x}\frac{\Delta x}{\Delta s}$$

and, from the diagram, we replace $\dfrac{\Delta x}{\Delta s}$ by $\cos\psi$ to give

$$\frac{\Delta\psi}{\Delta s} = \cos^2\psi D_x^2\phi(x, t)\times\cos\psi$$
$$= D_x^2\phi(x, t)\cos^3\psi.$$

But the equation of motion can be rearranged to give

$$\frac{\Delta\psi}{\Delta s} = \frac{\rho}{T\cos\psi}\, D_t^2\phi(x, t).$$

(This argument can be made more rigorous by considering formulae for ψ and s in terms of x – see the discussion of the length of a curve in M.T.) Thus

$$D_x^2\phi(x, t) = \frac{\rho}{T\cos^4\psi}\, D_t^2\phi(x, t).$$

If ψ is never very large, we make the approximation†

$$\cos^4\psi = 1,$$

and letting $c^2 = T/\rho$, we get the *wave equation*

$$D_x^2\phi(x, t) = \frac{1}{c^2}\, D_t^2\phi(x, t).$$

There is a general method for solving this sort of equation. It arises because of the fact that the two differential operators D_x and D_t have been separated and put one on each side of the equation. We try a solution of the form

$$\phi(x, t) = X(x).T(t),$$

i.e. we try to find a solution in which ϕ is expressed as the product of two functions **X** and **T**, which are functions of the single variables x and t respectively. Putting this assumption to the test, we see that

$$D^2X(x).T(t) = \frac{1}{c^2}\, D^2T(t).X(x),$$

† Since $\tan\psi = D_x\phi(x, t)\cos^2\psi = (1+[D_x\phi(x, t)]^2)^{-1}$, and so this approximation is equivalent to assuming that the oscillations are small enough to ignore $[D_x\phi(x, t)]^2$ compared with unity.

i.e.

$$\boxed{\frac{D^2X(x)}{X(x)} = \frac{1}{c^2}\frac{D^2T(t)}{T(t)}.}$$

Suppose we fix a value of t, say $t = 0$ to be definite, then we must have

$$\frac{D^2X(x)}{X(x)} = \frac{1}{c^2}\frac{D^2T(0)}{T(0)}.$$

We write this *constant* on the right-hand side as $-\lambda$, choosing the minus sign (by hindsight) for reasons which will become apparent. Then we have

$$D^2X(x) = -\lambda X(x)$$

or

$$D^2X(x) + \lambda X(x) = 0$$

which is just the Simple Harmonic Motion equation and therefore easy to solve. But how can we decide on the value of λ? Have we any data to fall back on? Let us consider the special case where ends of the string, at the points 0 and l, are fixed. Then we have

$$\phi(0, t) = \phi(l, t) = 0$$

whatever the value of t. Since the points 0 and l are at the ends of the interval on which we define x, we say that these conditions which we impose on the solutions are *boundary conditions*.

For this problem, then, the boundary conditions are

$$\phi(0, t) = \phi(l, t) = 0 \quad \text{for all values of } t.$$

Thus

$$X(0) = X(l) = 0.$$

How do these boundary conditions affect the possible choice of λ? The general solution of the equation

$$D^2X + \lambda X = 0$$

is

$$X(x) = A\cos\sqrt{\lambda}x + B\sin\sqrt{\lambda}x.$$

The boundary condition $X(0) = 0$ means that

$$A = 0.$$

The boundary condition $X(l) = 0$ means that

$$B\sin\sqrt{\lambda}l = 0.$$

Thus $$\sqrt{\lambda}l = n\pi$$

for some integer n, giving,

$$\lambda = \frac{n^2\pi^2}{l^2},$$

so that $$X(x) = B\sin\frac{n\pi}{l}x$$

for some integer n if both boundary conditions are to be satisfied. But the choice of n is still arbitrary. We can get a solution of the equation which satisfies the boundary conditions by choosing λ to be any one of the values

$$\frac{\pi^2}{l^2}, \quad \frac{2^2\pi^2}{l^2}, \quad \frac{3^2\pi^2}{l^2}, \quad \cdots, \quad \frac{n^2\pi^2}{l^2}, \quad \cdots.$$

These possible choices of λ are called the *eigenvalues* of the system.

Each eigenvalue determines a solution of the form

$$X(x) = B\sin\left(\frac{n\pi}{l}x\right)$$

which is unique to the choice $\frac{n^2\pi^2}{l^2}$ that has been made for λ. We call this function **X** an *eigenfunction* of the system. We have found possible forms for **X**, but from the equations

$$\frac{D^2X(x)}{X(x)} = \frac{1}{c^2}\frac{D^2T(t)}{T(t)} = -\lambda,$$

we also have an equation for **T**, which is

$$D^2T + c^2\lambda T = 0.$$

But we now have a limited choice for λ; it must have the form $\frac{n^2\pi^2}{l^2}$. Thus we get $$D^2T + \frac{c^2n^2\pi^2}{l^2}T = 0$$

which is the simple harmonic motion equation again. The general solution is

$$T(t) = a\cos\left(\frac{cn\pi}{l}t\right) + b\sin\left(\frac{cn\pi}{l}t\right),$$

where a and b are constants.

We started our investigation with the assumption that

$$\phi(x, t) = X(x)\, T(t),$$

and for this particular eigenvalue $\left(\lambda = \dfrac{n^2\pi^2}{l^2}\right)$, we have arrived at the solution

$$\phi(x, t) = B\sin\left(\frac{n\pi}{l}x\right)\left\{a\cos\left(\frac{cn\pi}{l}t\right) + b\,\sin\left(\frac{cn\pi}{l}t\right)\right\}.$$

This expression for $\phi(x, t)$ has the look of a general term of a Fourier Series about it, but there are two points to consider.

(i) We found that *any* of the eigenvalues $\dfrac{n^2\pi^2}{l^2}$, n an integer, was good enough to give us a solution which satisfied the boundary conditions.

(ii) If $\boldsymbol{\phi}_\alpha$ and $\boldsymbol{\phi}_\beta$ are both solutions of the equation

$$\mathrm{D}_x^2\boldsymbol{\phi} = \frac{1}{c^2}\,\mathrm{D}_t^2\boldsymbol{\phi}$$

then $\boldsymbol{\phi}_\alpha + \boldsymbol{\phi}_\beta$ is also a solution, since

$$\mathrm{D}_x^2(\boldsymbol{\phi}_\alpha + \boldsymbol{\phi}_\beta) = \mathrm{D}_n^2\boldsymbol{\phi}_\alpha + \mathrm{D}_n^2\boldsymbol{\phi}_\beta$$

$$= \frac{1}{c^2}\,\mathrm{D}_t^2\boldsymbol{\phi}_\alpha + \frac{1}{c^2}\,\mathrm{D}_t^2\boldsymbol{\phi}_\beta$$

$$= \frac{1}{c^2}\,\mathrm{D}_t^2(\boldsymbol{\phi}_\alpha + \boldsymbol{\phi}_\beta),$$

i.e. if we have any 2 solutions, then adding them gives us another solution.

So to obtain another, more general solution, we can add together each of the individual solutions that we obtained for each eigenvalue. The easiest way to write this is to denote the constants which correspond to an eigenvalue $\dfrac{n^2\pi^2}{2}$ by B_n, a_n and b_n instead of B, a and b. Then we can write another solution as

$$\phi(x, t) = \sum_{n=1}^{\infty} B_n\sin\left(\frac{n\pi}{l}x\right)\left\{a_n\cos\left(\frac{cn\pi}{l}t\right) + b_n\sin\left(\frac{cn\pi}{l}t\right)\right\}^\dagger$$

$$= \sum_{n=1}^{\infty}\phi_n(x, t).$$

† Notice that we have now lost the property that $\phi(x, t) = X(x)\,.\,T(t)$, but this is of no concern; the assumption was made to obtain a solution, which we did. We then found that we had many of them and could add them together.

But can we decide whether this is *the* general solution? You may have noticed that it follows quite easily from Note (ii) above that the set of all solutions forms a vector space. The general solution will be one vector in this space. Thus one way to find it is to devise a way of writing it as a vector in this space. The way this is usually done is to find a basis for the space. The only snag here is that the dimension of this space is not finite. This can be seen by noting that the functions ϕ_n that we have found are linearly independent and form an infinite set. Perhaps, then, this is a suitable basis. In fact it is – but the situation is not quite as easy as that – not every infinite set of independent vectors form a basis for an infinite dimensional space. Consider, for example, the vector space which has been the main concern of this book – the space of linear combinations of the **cos m** and **sin n** functions. In this space, the **cos m** functions form an infinite, independent set of vectors. But they certainly do not form a basis for the space; no odd function can be expressed in terms of them. The whole question of when and how one gets a basis for solution spaces of this type is tied up with the general theory of *boundary value problems* and is not our primary concern in this book although we do make some tentative excursions in this direction in the next chapter. For the moment, we ask you to take it on trust that the above expression does represent *the* general solution.

Returning to our problem, it looks even more like a Fourier Series, but we still have some undetermined constants B_n, a_n and b_n in the expression. To find these, we need more data. This usually comes from knowing something about the configuration of the string at a particular time, usually at the moment it is set vibrating.

A typical situation at time $t = 0$ might be this:

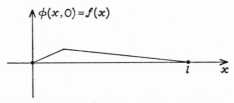

The string is pulled at some point, held stationary, and we start counting the seconds from the moment the string is released. These

93

boundary conditions can be expressed mathematically by the following equations.

$$\left.\begin{array}{l} \phi(x, 0) = f(x), \\ D_t\phi(x, 0) = 0, \end{array}\right\} \quad (x \in [0, l]).$$

Let us have a look at the implications of the second condition which corresponds to the initial velocity of the string being zero.

$$D_t\phi(x, 0) = \sum_{n=1}^{\infty} B_n \sin\left(\frac{n\pi}{l}x\right)\left\{-a_n \frac{cn\pi}{l}\sin\left(\frac{cn\pi}{l}t\right)\right.$$

$$\left.+b_n \frac{cn\pi}{l}\cos\left(\frac{cn\pi}{l}t\right)\right\}$$

which is zero for all values of $x \in [0, l]$. Thus

$$b_n = 0 \quad \text{for all } n.$$

Going back to the expression for ϕ, this now becomes

$$\phi(x, t) = \sum_{n=1}^{\infty} a_n B_n \sin\left(\frac{n\pi}{l}x\right)\cos\left(\frac{cn\pi}{l}t\right)$$

and, using the first boundary condition,

$$\phi(x, 0) = \sum_{n=1}^{\infty} a_n B_n \sin\left(\frac{n\pi}{l}x\right)$$

$$= f(x).$$

Thus the constants $(a_n B_n)$ are Fourier coefficients of **f**. We have to decide which Fourier Series of **f**, and clearly it has to be the Fourier Sine Series. So we will need to extend the domain of **f** to be the interval $[-l, l]$ and extend **f** in such a way that we get an odd function. All that is left is to find the Fourier Sine Series of **f**, and this will tell us the value of the constants $a_n B_n$. Once we have found $a_n B_n$, which in theory at least we can do because we know **f**, the problem is completely solved.

Some readers may be interested in a recap of one feature of what we have done in this case study. We started with a partial differential equation which has an infinite number of solutions, which form a vector space, S say.

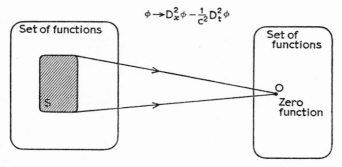

If we have a physical problem to solve then we clearly do not want an infinite number of answers. But a physical problem usually has physical restraints, and the first of these were the boundary conditions. In other words the boundary conditions picked out a subset of S – the set of solutions ϕ_n.

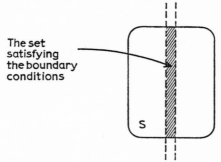

The set satisfying the boundary conditions

But there are still an infinite number of solutions here. Another subset of S is specified by the initial conditions, and what is remarkable is that,

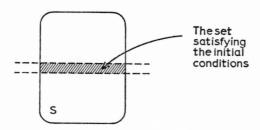

The set satisfying the initial conditions

although one could find a whole infinite set of solutions to satisfy these initial conditions, there is just one *unique solution* which satisfies both the initial conditions *and* the boundary conditions.

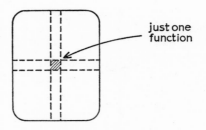

just one
function

One of the objects of the study of partial differential equations is to investigate just what type of initial and boundary conditions lead to this happy state of affairs.

Case Study 4   The Heat Equation (1)

The situations covered by the heat equation can be derived from one simple case. We consider a thin metal wire which is heavily lagged so that heat only flows along the wire.

The two variables on which we assume the temperature depends are

position along the rod $x \in [0, l]$
and the time $\quad\quad\quad t \in \mathbf{R}_0^+$

and we use the function ϕ to express the temperature as $\phi(x, t)$. The fact that there is only one position variable corresponds to the fact that the wire is lagged, and so the temperature is assumed to be constant over any cross-section. The heat equation expressses the way in which the temperature changes with time along the wire.

It is obtained by assuming three physical laws:

(i) Fourier's Law. The quantity of heat that flows across any cross-section of the rod is proportional to the rate of change of temperature across that section.

(ii) The amount of heat gained by a body equals the specific heat times the mass times the rise in temperature.

(iii) The law of conservation of heat. For any body,

the gain of heat = input of heat − output of heat.

We look at the way the temperature changes in a small element of the wire.

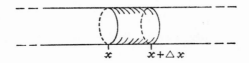

Consider (i). The rate of change of temperature across the section is $D_x \phi(x, t)$. We know that heat flows from hot to cold, that is, in the direction of decreasing temperature. Thus a positive quantity of heat will flow across the section if the rate of change of temperature, $D_x\phi(x, t)$, is negative. Fourier's Law states that these two quantities are proportional, and so the quantity of heat entering the element is

$$H_1 = -KD_x\phi(x, t) \quad (K < 0),$$

where K is the constant of proportionality. Similarly the quantity of heat leaving the element is

$$H_2 = -KD_x\phi(x+\Delta x, t).$$

Now consider (ii). The gain of heat is

$$H_3 = k\,\Delta x\,D_t\phi(x, t)$$

where k is the density of the material x, its specific heat. Finally, consider (iii). This tells us that

$$H_3 = H_1 - H_2$$

i.e. $$k\,\Delta x D_t\phi(x, t) = K(D_x\phi(x+\Delta x, t) - D_x\phi(x, t)),$$

i.e. $$D_t\phi(x, t) = c\,\frac{D_x\phi(x+\Delta x, t) - D_x\phi(x, t)}{\Delta x},$$

where $c = \dfrac{K}{k}$. Letting $\Delta x \sim 0$, we get the one-dimensional heat equation,

$$D_x^2\phi(x, t) = \frac{1}{c}\,D_t\phi(x, t),$$

where c is constant determined by the physical characteristics of the material. To solve the heat equation, we assume, as in Case Study 3, that ϕ can be expressed as the product of two functions

$$\phi(x, t) = X(x)\,T(t)$$

so that we can separate the variables. Then

$$\frac{D^2X(x)}{X(x)} = \frac{1}{c}\,\frac{DT(t)}{T(t)} = -\lambda,$$

λ being a constant which we can choose later. Considering $X(x)$ first, we get

$$D^2X(x) + \lambda X(x) = 0.$$

We saw in Case Study 3 that the boundary conditions played an important part in the way in which we choose λ. It is the same here.

Suppose, for example that the wire is warmed up before the start of an experiment, and that both ends of the wire are dipped into buckets of ice when $t = 0$. This will give us the boundary condition

$$\phi(0, t) = \phi(l, t) = 0 \quad \text{for all } t > 0.$$

Thus $$X(0) = X(t) = 0.$$

These boundary conditions give eigenvalues for λ as

$$\left(\frac{\pi}{l}\right), \quad \left(\frac{2\pi}{l}\right)^2, \quad \left(\frac{3\pi}{l}\right)^2, \quad ..., \quad \left(\frac{n\pi}{l}\right)^2, \quad ...$$

and the corresponding eigenfunctions

$$X(x) = B\sin\left(\frac{n\pi}{l}x\right) \quad \text{[See Case Study 3].}$$

With each eigenvalue $\lambda = \left(\frac{n\pi}{l}\right)^2$, we get the corresponding differential equation for t which is

$$DT(t) + \frac{cn^2\pi^2}{l^2}T(t) = 0.$$

The general solution of this equation is

$$T(t) = a\exp\left(-\frac{cn^2\pi^2}{l^2}t\right).$$

Thus for each eigenvalue we get a solution

$$\phi(x, t) = Ba\sin\left(\frac{n\pi}{l}x\right)\exp\left(-\frac{cn^2\pi^2}{l^2}t\right).$$

And we obtain the general solution by adding together the solutions obtained for each eigenvalue.

$$\phi(x, t) = \sum_{n=1}^{\infty} B_n a_n \sin\left(\frac{n\pi}{l}x\right)\exp\left(-\frac{cn^2\pi^2}{l^2}t\right).$$

We can find the constants $B_n a_n$ if the initial temperature is given. Thus if $$\phi(x, 0) = f(x) \quad (x \in [0, l]).$$

We write $$f(x) = \sum_{n=1}^{\infty} B_n a_n \sin\left(\frac{n\pi}{l}x\right)\exp\left(-\frac{cn^2\pi^2}{l^2}t\right),$$

and we determine each constant $B_n a_n$ by setting it equal to the corresponding coefficient of **f** in the Fourier Sine Series for **f**. Thus

$$B_n a_n = \frac{2}{l} \int_0^l f(x) \sin \left(\frac{n\pi}{l} x \right) dx.$$

This completes the solution.

You may have noticed that in this case we have only one initial condition, whereas for the wave equation we required two initial conditions; the initial configuration of the string and the initial velocity of the string. This difference is accounted for by the fact that in the heat equation, the derivative with respect to t is a first order one, and in the wave equation we have a second order derivative with respect to time. Consequently on separating the variables we have a first order ordinary differential equation in one instance (requiring only one condition to give a unique solution) and a second order equation in the other case (requiring two conditions).

Case Study 5 **The Heat Equation (2)**

As our last case study we take again the situation of the conduction of heat along a thin, well insulated rod but this time with different boundary conditions. We shall see that this gives rise to a different type of Fourier Series.

We shall have the same equation;

$$D_x^2 \phi(x, t) = \frac{1}{c} D_t \phi(x, t) = -\lambda^2,$$

and the same type of initial condition

$$\phi(x, 0) = f(x) \quad (x \in [0, l]),$$

where f is some given function, and the same boundary condition at $x = 0$,
$$\phi(0, t) = 0 \quad (t \in R_0^+).$$

But let us suppose this time that the end at $x = l$ is not fixed at some temperature, but just left exposed to the air. Further let us suppose that the air is at a temperature of zero. (This just simplifies the arithmetic and amounts simply to a shift of scale.) To model this situation we assume that the rate of flow of heat out of the rod at this end is proportional to the difference in the temperature of the rod at that end and the air, i.e.

$$D_x \phi(l, t) = -h \phi(l, t)$$

where h is a positive constant. As far as the sign of h is concerned, heat will certainly flow out of the rod if $\phi(l, t) > 0$. This drop in temperature will entail a negative rate of change of temperature, i.e., if $\phi(l, t) > 0$, thus $D_x \phi(l, t) < 0$.

Now we can set about solving the problem. As before, we can separate the variables to give an ordinary differential equation for X;

$$D^2 X + \lambda^2 X = 0.$$

The boundary condition at $x = 0$ will again give us

$$X(0) = 0,$$

but at $x = l$ we get $\quad D X(l) = -h X(l).$

101

Solving the first equation for X gives

$$X(x) = A\cos\lambda x + B\sin\lambda x,$$

and using the condition at $x = 0$ we deduce that $A = 0$ and so

$$X(x) = B\sin\lambda x.$$

The permissible values of λ are obtained by substituting this in the boundary condition at $x = l$. This gives

$$B\lambda\cos\lambda l = -hB\sin\lambda l,$$

and so λ must statisfy the equation

$$\tan\lambda l = -\frac{\lambda}{h}.$$

If we plot the graphs with equations

$$y = -\frac{\lambda}{h}, \quad y = \tan\lambda l,$$

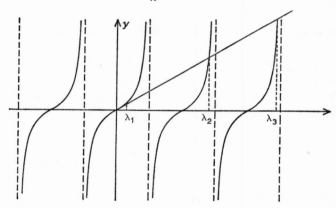

we see that we get an infinite number of solutions for λ. If we denote by λ_n the nth solution, then we see that we get solutions of the form

$$X_n(x) = B_n\sin\lambda_n x,$$

where, as in other case studies, we used suffices to denote solutions and constants appropriate to a particular eigenvalue.

To find the T part of the solution we have to solve the equation

$$DT(t) + c\lambda^2 T(t) = 0,$$

where the λ now has to be one of these special eigenvalues. This gives

$$T_n(t) = a_n \exp(c\lambda_n^2 t).$$

Combining this solution with $X_n(t)$ we get a solution for the temperature;

$$\phi(x, t) = \sum_{n=1}^{\infty} b_n \sin \lambda_n x \exp(-c\lambda_n^2 t),$$

where $b_n = B_n a_n$.

We are still left with the problem of calculating b_n, and, as before, we hope to do this by using the initial condition, which gives

$$f(x) = \sum_{n=1}^{\infty} b_n \sin \lambda_n x.$$

This looks much the same sort of problem as we were left with before; the b_n's are just the Fourier coefficients of **f**. But wait a minute! This time, the λ_n's have not got the simple form that we had before and the $\sin \lambda_n x$ terms are not the usual **sinn** functions that we have previously used for Fourier Series, nor are they functions of the form

$$x \to \sin \frac{n\pi}{L} x.$$

(Look carefully at the graph.)

But all is not lost if we remember that a Fourier Series is a possibility in terms of *any* infinite orthogonal set, the move to make is obviously to see whether the set of functions $\{x \to \sin \lambda_n x\}$ is orthogonal in $[0, l]$.

There are no prizes for guessing that they are orthogonal, why else would we be bothering! This can be confirmed by straightforward integration. Suppose λ_i and λ_j are two of the permissible eigenvalues and are unequal. Then we wish to consider

$$\int_0^l \sin \lambda_i x \sin \lambda_j x \, dx$$

$$= \int_0^l \tfrac{1}{2} \{\cos(\lambda_i - \lambda_j)x - \cos(\lambda_i + \lambda_j)x\} \, dx$$

$$= \frac{1}{2} \left[\frac{\sin(\lambda_i - \lambda_j)x}{\lambda_i - \lambda_j} - \frac{\sin(\lambda_i + \lambda_j)x}{\lambda_i + \lambda_j} \right]_0^l$$

$$= \frac{1}{2(\lambda_i^2 - \lambda_j^2)} \{(\lambda_i + \lambda_j)\sin(\lambda_i - \lambda_j)l - (\lambda_i - \lambda_j)\sin(\lambda_i + \lambda_j)l\}.$$

Using the identity

$$\sin(A+B) = \sin A \cos B + \sin B \cos A$$

and collecting up the pieces afterwards, we get

$$\int_0^l \sin\lambda_i x \sin\lambda_j x \, dx$$
$$= \frac{1}{2(\lambda_i^2 - \lambda_j^2)} \{2\lambda_i \sin\lambda_i l \cos\lambda_j l - 2\lambda_j \sin\lambda_j l \cos\lambda_i l\}.$$

This can be simplified by using the fact the λ_i and λ_j satisfy the equation

$$\tan\lambda l = -\frac{\lambda}{h}.$$

In other words, $$\sin\lambda_i l = -\frac{\lambda_i \cos\lambda_i l}{h}$$

and $$\sin\lambda_j l = -\frac{\lambda_j \cos\lambda_j l}{h}.$$

If you substitute these expressions into the result of the integration, you will find that 'simplification' was an understatement – it reduces to zero. In other words the functions do form an orthogonal set in $[0, l]$. If we put

$$\int_0^l \sin^2\lambda_i x \, dx = k_i,$$

then the set of functions $\left\{x \to \dfrac{\sin\lambda_i x}{k_i}\right\}$ are orthonormal and can play the role of $\{\phi_i\}$ in the arguments of Chapter 3. Hence the coefficients b_n can be found, at least in theory, because f is a known function, and the problem is solved.

The mathematical method of solution is essentially no different from the other cases. Of course, we have made all sorts of assumptions in obtaining the solution. Results which we have proved about trigonometric Fourier Series, we have assumed can be carried over to this case. So a careful analysis is really called for, but that is not our concern here. For our purposes, the interest lies in the possibility of extending our work to more general situations.

6 · Some General Remarks

Much of what we have seen in this book is a particular example of a very general area of mathematics. The idea of expanding a function in terms of the eigenfunctions of a linear differential operator can be applied to a number of different situations. The conditions under which those eigenfunctions are orthogonal can be stated in very general terms and leads us to the idea of a symmetric operator.

In the last three case studies of the Chapter 5, it may have occurred to you that there was a striking similarity between the mathematical themes of each argument. This chapter is about some of the general principles involved. From the historical point of view, Fourier's work was of immense significance to mathematics. For it constituted the first step along the road towards a very general theory of 'approximating a given function by a sequence of other functions'.

But Fourier's approach to the theory was very different from that presented in this book – the benefit of hindsight is on our side. If you read this chapter with the sense that you are looking ahead to a more sophisticated solution of the general problem that we started with, then you will be well on the way to understanding a large and extremely important branch of mathematics, and one that is absolutely dripping with applications.

Although it is where the way ahead lies, this book is no place to develop a methodical treatment of differential equations and boundary value problems – for one thing such a task demands a greater knowledge of linear algebra and analysis than we have assumed. Nevertheless those points which relate to some of the things we have met in this book may be of interest.

The separation of the variables method led to equations of the form

$$(D^2 + \lambda) \, X(x) = 0,$$

where λ was a constant introduced by the process of separating the variables. This type of equation has solutions of the form

$$X(x) = \cos\sqrt{\lambda}x,$$
$$X(x) = \sin\sqrt{\lambda}x,$$

where the possible values that λ could take were determined by boundary conditions, giving

$$\lambda_1, \lambda_2, \lambda_3, \ldots, \lambda_n, \ldots.$$

We were then led to a solution of the original partial differential equation with a form such as

$$\phi(x, t) = \sum_{n=1}^{\infty} (A_n\cos\sqrt{\lambda_n}x + B_n\sin\sqrt{\lambda_n}x)\, T(\lambda_n, t),$$

where the summation is over all the values of n which give all possible values of λ_n. The coefficients A_n and B_n were calculated by using an 'initial' condition, i.e. a specification of $\phi(x, t)$ for some given value of t. This produced a formula of the form

$$f(x) = \sum_{n=1}^{\infty} (A_n\cos\sqrt{\lambda_n}x + B_n\sin\sqrt{\lambda_n}x).$$

In several of the case studies, the λ_n's were of the form $\dfrac{n^2\pi^2}{l^2}$ and so the A_n's and B_n's were simply Fourier coefficients of the function **f**. But in Case Study 5, the λ_n's were not of this form and, strictly speaking, the methods of calculating Fourier Series were of no use in the solution of the problem. But the similarity suggested how to proceed and it transpired that the functions $\cos\sqrt{\lambda_n}x$ and $\sin\sqrt{\lambda_n}x$ formed an orthogonal set. The Fourier procedure could be carried out in a formal way to produce a solution. This generalisation of Fourier Series prompts two questions:

'Are there any other orthogonal sets of functions?'

and in the context of boundary conditions which determine the value of λ_n,

'What sort of boundary conditions will give orthogonal sets of functions?'

Before we consider these two questions in a general context, we shall answer the first by giving two specific examples of such sets of functions.

Example 1

Show that the functions $\mathbf{P_n}$ (the Legendre polynomials) with domain $[-1, 1]$ defined by

$$\mathbf{P_0} = x \to 1,$$

$$\mathbf{P_n} = \frac{1}{2^n n!} \, \mathrm{D}^n(x \to (x^2 - 1)^n)$$

form an orthogonal set.

Solution

We have

$$\mathbf{P_m} \cdot \mathbf{P_n} = \int_{-1}^{1} \frac{1}{2^n n!} \, \mathrm{D}^n(x^2 - 1)^n \, \frac{1}{2^m m!} \, \mathrm{D}^m(x^2 - 1)^m \, \mathrm{d}x$$

and successive integration by parts will produce the required result.

Exercise 1

Prove $\mathbf{P_m} \cdot \mathbf{P_n} = 0$ when $m \neq n$.

Example 2

The Legendre polynomials are orthogonal with respect to the scalar product which we have been using for Fourier Series. But we have a lot more room to manoeuvre because we can invent all sorts of inner product. For example, with respect to the inner product

$$\mathbf{f} \cdot \mathbf{g} = \int_{-\infty}^{\infty} \mathrm{e}^{-x^2/2} f(x) g(x) \, \mathrm{d}x$$

the Hermite polynomials, defined by

$$H_n(x) = (-1)^n \mathrm{e}^{x^2/2} \mathrm{D}^n(\mathrm{e}^{-x^2/2}) \quad (x \in \mathbb{R}),$$

form an orthogonal set.

Exercise 2

Prove that $\mathbf{H_m} \cdot \mathbf{H_n} = 0$ when $m \neq n$.

Proof of the fact that $\mathbf{f} \cdot \mathbf{g}$, as we have defined it here, *is* a scalar product is not a triviality. However, it is not our purpose here to chase after as many different orthogonal sets or scalar products as possible. We shall see in later exercises how the Legendre and Hermite polynomials arise.

107

The equation $$D^2X + \lambda X = 0$$

is a particular case of the general equation

$$LX = \lambda X,$$

where L is a linear operator (in this case, $L = -D^2$). The essential properties of L are that it is a function whose domain is a vector space of functions and that

$$L(\lambda u + \mu v) = \lambda Lu + \mu Lv \tag{1}$$

for any **u** and **v** in the domain and any scalars λ and μ.

Example 3

The differential operators D^2, $D^2 + 2$, $3D^2 - 4D + 1$, and so on, are all examples of linear operators on a suitable vector space of functions. So are the following:

$$Lf(x) = f(x+h) - f(x),$$

$$Lf(x) = \frac{f(x) + f(-x)}{2},$$

$$Lf(x) = xf(x).$$

The problem of finding the values of λ for which the equation

$$LX = \lambda X$$

has solutions other than $X = 0$ is called the *eigenvalue problem* for the operator L. Such values of λ are called eigenvalues of L and the corresponding solutions **X** are called eigenvectors or, in spaces of functions, eigenfunctions of the operator L. In our case studies, we met several examples of this type and the eigenfunctions formed orthogonal sets. So let us investigate the general statement of the problem with an eye on orthogonality.

Suppose we have a scalar product which is defined on the domain of a linear operator L and also on the image space. Suppose further that λ_1 and λ_2 are two eigenvalues of L with corresponding eigenfunctions X_1 and X_2. We are interested in whether or not X_1 and X_2 are othogonal. Then

$$LX_1 = \lambda_1 X_1,$$

$$LX_2 = \lambda_2 X_2,$$

giving
$$\mathbf{X_1.X_2} = \frac{1}{\lambda_1}((L\mathbf{X_1}).\mathbf{X_2})$$

and
$$\mathbf{X_1.X_2} = \frac{1}{\lambda_2}(\mathbf{X_1}.(L\mathbf{X_2})).$$

Thus
$$(\lambda_1-\lambda_2)(\mathbf{X_1.X_2}) = (L\mathbf{X_1.X_2})-(\mathbf{X_1}.L\mathbf{X_2})$$

and we can conclude that, since $\lambda_1 \neq \lambda_2$,

$$(\mathbf{X_1.X_2}) = 0$$

if
$$(L\mathbf{X_1.X_2}) = (\mathbf{X_1}.L\mathbf{X_2}).$$

This last equation is one which may or may not be satisfied by any particular linear operator. If L has this property for every pair of elements $\mathbf{X_1}$ and $\mathbf{X_2}$ in its domain (not just eigenvectors) it is called *symmetric*. Thus if an operator is symmetric it certainly follows that the eigenvectors form an orthogonal set.

But this is a rather restrictive condition on L to ensure orthogonality. Indeed we know that it is unnecessarily restrictive, because we have already seen that if L is the operator $-D^2$ then we can certainly get orthogonal eigenfunctions. But $-D^2$ is not symmetric when its domain is any set of suitably differentiable functions S. As illustration of this, take the functions **f** and **g**, for example, where

$$\left.\begin{aligned}\mathbf{f}: x &\to x^2\\ \mathbf{g}: x &\to e^x\end{aligned}\right\} \quad (x \in [a, b]).$$

In this case,
$$L\mathbf{f.g} = \int_a^b -2e^x\,\mathrm{d}x$$
$$= 2(e^a-e^b),$$

and
$$\mathbf{f}.L\mathbf{g} = \int_a^b -x^2e^x\,\mathrm{d}x$$
$$= -(b^2-2b+2)e^b+(a^2-2a+2)e^a.$$

Thus
$$(L\mathbf{f.g}) \neq (\mathbf{f}.L\mathbf{g}).$$

However, taking any two functions **f** and **g** in this arbitrary domain S of the operator, we have,

$$L\mathbf{f.g} = \int_a^b -D^2f(x)g(x)\,\mathrm{d}x$$

and
$$\mathbf{f}.L\mathbf{g} = \int_a^b f(x)-D^2g(x)\,\mathrm{d}x.$$

Thus, on integrating by parts twice, we get

$$\mathbf{Lf.g} = \left[-Df(x)g(x)+f(x)Dg(x) \right]_a^b \ -\int_a^b f(x)D^2g(x)dx$$

$$= [-Df(x)g(x)+f(x)Dg(x)]_a^b+\mathbf{f.Lg}$$

and so, $\qquad\qquad\qquad \mathbf{Lf.g} = \mathbf{f.Lg}$

whenever $\qquad\qquad -[Df(x)g(x)+f(x)Dg(x)]_a^b = 0.$

So if we restrict the domain of $-D^2$ to those functions having this property, $-D^2$ is symmetric. It should be clear to you how important it is to specify the domain of a function!

In the case studies of the previous chapter we in effect restricted the domains of the differential operators to those functions which satisfied the boundary conditions, and this was a perfectly satisfactory device because the solution we sought was in that restricted domain.

The fact that the eigenfunctions turned out to be orthogonal means that, on those restricted domains, the differential operators were symmetric.

There is, in fact, a well developed theory to deal with more general differential operators than $-D^2$. For example, if the functions $\mathbf{p}$ and $\mathbf{q}$ satisfy certain conditions ($\mathbf{q}$ must be continuous, and $\mathbf{p}$ must be differentiable with $D\mathbf{p}$ continuous and $p(x) > 0$ for all x or $p(x) < 0$ for all x) then the differential operator

$$L = D[pD]+\mathbf{q}$$

is symmetric if the domain of L consists of functions such that

$$[p(x)\,(Df(x)g(x)-f(x)Dg(x))]_a^b = 0.$$

[The a and the b imply that the scalar product is

$$\mathbf{f.g} = \int_a^b f(x)g(x)dx].$$

You may like to prove that L is symmetric in this case by following a very similar argument to the one used previously.

In fact, subject to the same conditions for symmetry, we can also get orthogonal sets of functions with respect to a more general inner product. The eigenfunctions of the generalised eigenvalue problem

$$\mathbf{Lf} = \lambda\mathbf{rf},$$

(where $r(x) \geqslant 0$, and $r(x) = 0$ only at a finite number of points in $[a, b]$) are orthogonal with respect to the inner product

$$\mathbf{f.g} = \int_a^b r(x)f(x)g(x)\,\mathrm{d}x.$$

Exercise 3

(i) Show that the equation

$$(1 - x)^2 \mathbf{D}^2 f(x) - 2x \mathbf{D}f(x) + n(n+1) f(x) = 0$$

can be written in the form

$$\mathbf{D}[\mathbf{p}\,\mathbf{D}\mathbf{f}] + \mathbf{q}\mathbf{f} = \lambda \mathbf{r}\mathbf{f},$$

where $\lambda = n(n+1)$ and hence deduce that the Legendre Polynomials (see Example 1) are orthogonal.

[*Hint.* Use the definition of $\mathbf{P}_n$ to show that $\mathbf{P}_n$ is the eigenfunction for the given value $\lambda = n(n+1)$.]

(ii) Show that the equation

$$\mathbf{D}^2 g(x) - x \mathbf{D}g(x) + ng(x) = 0$$

can be written in the form

$$\mathbf{D}[\mathbf{p}\,\mathbf{D}\mathbf{g}] + \mathbf{q}\mathbf{g} = \lambda \mathbf{r}\mathbf{g},$$

where $\lambda = n$ and hence deduce that the Hermite Polynomials (see Exercise 2) are orthogonal.

[*Hint.* Much the same as for part (i).]

Exercise 4

We have seen in Case Study 3 of the last chapter that the operator $-\mathbf{D}^2$ is symmetric on a space of functions with domain $[0, l]$ satisfying

$$f(0) = f(l) = 0.$$

Show that the restriction

$$f'(0) = f'(l) = 0$$

is also sufficient. Think of some examples of other boundary conditions which would make $-\mathbf{D}^2$ symmetric on $[0, l]$.

Find the eigenfunctions in each case.

It appears, then, that the methods we have developed in this book for finding Fourier Series have a much wider application than expanding functions as trigonometric series. The possibility of finding trigonometric series hinged on the fact that the **cos m** and **sin n** functions form an orthogonal set. But we now see that much more general problems can lead to orthogonal sets of functions and that Fourier-type expansions can be used to solve a very general class of differential equations. The process is as follows.

If L is a symmetric differential operator we can, at least formally, proceed to a solution of the equation

$$\mathbf{Lf} = \mathbf{h}.$$

For, if the eigenfunctions, ϕ_0, ϕ_1, ϕ_2, ϕ_3, ... form a *basis* for the vector space under consideration, then we can write

$$\mathbf{h} = \sum_{i=0}^{\infty} \alpha_i \phi_i$$

and

$$\alpha_i = \frac{\mathbf{h} \cdot \phi_i}{\phi_i \cdot \phi_i}.$$

The values a_i can be found by applying a similar procedure to the one developed in Chapter 3. Since the ϕ_i's form a basis, we know that we can write the solution we are looking for in the form

$$\mathbf{f} = \sum_{i=0}^{\infty} \beta_i \phi_i.$$

Substituting this into the differential equation gives

$$\mathbf{L} \sum_{i=0}^{\infty} \beta_i \phi_i = \sum_{i=0}^{\infty} \alpha_i \phi_i.$$

Usually, we can distribute the operator L throughout the summation and we get

$$\sum_{i=0}^{\infty} \beta_i \mathbf{L} \phi_i = \sum_{i=0}^{\infty} \alpha_i \phi_i$$

and if λ_i is the eigenvalue corresponding to ϕ_i we get

$$\sum_{i=0}^{\infty} \beta_i \lambda_i \phi_i = \sum_{i=0}^{\infty} \alpha_i \phi_i.$$

Since the ϕ_i's are linearly independent we conclude that

$$\beta_i = \frac{\alpha_i}{\lambda_i}$$

and that the solution of the equation is

$$\mathbf{f} = \sum_{i=0}^{\infty} \frac{\alpha_i}{\lambda_i} \phi_i.$$

Of course this formal development is riddled with assumptions!

First of all we assumed that the eigenfunctions form a basis. Textbooks on differential equations give the conditions which must prevail to ensure this.

Secondly, the formula
$$\beta_i = \frac{\alpha_i}{\lambda_i}$$

means that there may be trouble if any of the eigenvalues are zero. If one of the eigenvalues is zero then it turns out that the operator L is not one-one, and so we cannot expect a unique solution.

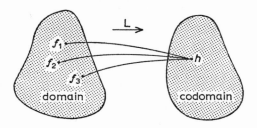

If, for example, $\lambda_k = 0$, then if $\alpha_k = 0$ also there will be an infinite number of solutions. But if $\alpha_k \neq 0$ there will be no solution.

Thirdly, even if we can get to the last step and write

$$\mathbf{f} = \sum_{i=0}^{\infty} \frac{\alpha_i}{\lambda_i} \phi_i$$

this will only be a solution if it can be substituted back into the equation. That is to say, it must be in the domain of L: if L is a differential operator then it means that it must be possible to differentiate the series an appropriate number of times and this will depend on the nature of **h** and the ϕ_i's. To cope with these problems, one requires a mixture of mathematics which involves both the general theory of linear operators, and the particular analysis of the case in hand. The work we have gone through in this book has attempted to show you both sides of the coin. In conclusion, we hope that you will have got the impression that this chapter is more of a beginning than an end.

Solutions to Exercises in the Text

Chapter 1

1. (i) The constant a has no bearing on the period of

$$x \rightarrow \sin \pi(x-a).$$

We know that the period of $x \rightarrow \sin x$ is 2π, hence the required period is 2.

(ii) Writing $\cos^2 x = \frac{1}{2}(\cos 2x + 1)$

it is easy to spot that this function has period π.

(iii) This function is not periodic.

Chapter 2

1. If **f** and **g** belong to $\mathscr{F}$, then each can be written most simply in terms of their general terms

$$\mathbf{f} = \ldots + a_m \cos \mathbf{m} + \ldots b_n \sin \mathbf{n} + \ldots,$$

$$\mathbf{g} = \ldots + \alpha_m \cos \mathbf{m} + \ldots + \beta_n \sin \mathbf{n} + \ldots.$$

Then adding like terms we get

$$\mathbf{f} + \mathbf{g} = \ldots + (a_m + \alpha_m) \cos \mathbf{m} + \ldots + (b_n + \beta_n) \sin \mathbf{n} + \ldots$$

and since $a_m + \alpha_m$, $b_n + \beta_n \in \mathrm{R}$, $\mathbf{f} + \mathbf{g} \in \mathscr{F}$. Also, if we multiply **f** by a real number α, since αa_m, $\alpha b_n \in \mathrm{R}$, we have $\alpha \mathbf{f} \in \mathscr{F}$.

2. (i) $$\mathbf{f} . \mathbf{f} = \int_{-\pi}^{\pi} f^2(x) \mathrm{d}x$$

and since the integrand, $f^2(x)$, is either positive or zero, the area under the graph of $f^2(x)$ is positive unless $f^2(x) = 0$ for all $x \in [-\pi, \pi]$.†
If $f^2(x) = 0$ for all such x, then $\mathbf{f} = \mathbf{0}$.

(ii) $$\mathbf{f} . \mathbf{g} = \int_{-\pi}^{\pi} f(x)g(x) \mathrm{d}x$$

$$= \int_{-\pi}^{\pi} g(x)f(x) \mathrm{d}x$$

$$= \mathbf{g} . \mathbf{f}.$$

† To be strictly accurate, we should have said 'for *almost* all $x \in [-\pi, \pi]$.' This is a technical term which need not bother us here; if you are interested, you will find it defined and a discussion of its relevance in most books on analysis.

(iii) $\mathbf{f}.(\alpha\mathbf{g}+\beta\mathbf{h}) = \displaystyle\int_{-\pi}^{\pi} f(x)\,(\alpha g(x)+\beta h(x))\,\mathrm{d}x$

$$= \int_{-\pi}^{\pi} (\alpha f(x)g(x)+\beta f(x)h(x))\,\mathrm{d}x$$

$$= \alpha \int_{-\pi}^{\pi} f(x)\,g(x)\,\mathrm{d}x + \beta \int_{-\pi}^{\pi} f(x)\,h(x)\,\mathrm{d}x$$

$$= \alpha\mathbf{f}.\mathbf{g}+\beta\mathbf{f}.\mathbf{h}.$$

3. Using the hint, we know

$$(\mathbf{u}+\lambda\mathbf{v}).(\mathbf{u}+\lambda\mathbf{v}) \geqslant 0,$$

$$\mathbf{u}.\mathbf{u}+2\lambda\mathbf{u}.\mathbf{v}+\lambda^2\mathbf{v}.\mathbf{v} \geqslant 0.$$

Considering this inequality for any real number λ this form should remind you of an equation like

$$ax^2+bx+c = 0$$

with λ for x, which has not got two distinct roots if

$$b^2 \leqslant 4ac.$$

So that $\qquad\qquad (2\mathbf{u}.\mathbf{v})^2 \leqslant 4(\mathbf{v}.\mathbf{v})\,(\mathbf{u}.\mathbf{u}),$

i.e. $\qquad\qquad (\mathbf{u}.\mathbf{v})^2 \leqslant (\mathbf{u}.\mathbf{u})\,(\mathbf{v}.\mathbf{v}).$

4. The scalar product of (i) has the properties (ii) and (iii), but not (i). The scalar products of (ii) and (iii) have all three properties.

5. (i) $\mathbf{1}.\mathbf{1} = \displaystyle\int_{-\pi}^{\pi} 1\,\mathrm{d}x$

$$= 2\pi.$$

(ii) $\mathbf{cos\,m}.\mathbf{cos\,m} = \displaystyle\int_{-\pi}^{\pi} \cos^2 mx\,\mathrm{d}x$

$$= \int_{-\pi}^{\pi} \tfrac{1}{2}(\cos 2mx+1)\,\mathrm{d}x$$

$$= \left[\frac{1}{2}\left(\frac{1}{2m}\sin 2mx+x\right)\right]_{-\pi}^{\pi}$$

$$= \pi.$$

(iii) $\mathbf{sinn.sinn} = \displaystyle\int_{-\pi}^{\pi} \sin^2 nx\,dx$

$$= \int_{-\pi}^{\pi} \tfrac{1}{2}(1-\cos 2nx)\,dx$$

$$= \pi.$$

Chapter 3

1. (i) This is an odd function, so we need only work out

Step 3 $\quad b_n = \dfrac{2}{\pi}\displaystyle\int_0^{\pi} 2x\sin nx\,dx$

$$= \dfrac{4}{\pi}\left\{\left[-\dfrac{1}{n}x\cos nx\right]_0^{\pi} + \dfrac{1}{n}\int_0^{\pi}\cos nx\,dx\right\}$$

$$= \dfrac{4}{\pi}\left\{\dfrac{-\pi(-1)^n}{n} + 0\right\}.$$

Thus $\qquad\qquad \mathbf{f} \simeq 4\left\{\sin - \dfrac{\sin 2}{2} + \dfrac{\sin 3}{3} - \ldots\right\}.$

Compare this with Example 1; the result is hardly surprising!

(ii) This is an even function, so we need only work out

Step 1 $\quad a_0 = \dfrac{2}{2\pi}\displaystyle\int_0^{\pi} 3\,dx$

$$= 3.$$

Step 2 $\quad a_m = \dfrac{2}{\pi}\displaystyle\int_0^{\pi} 3\cos mx\,dx$

$$= \dfrac{2}{\pi}\left[\dfrac{3}{m}\sin mx\right]_0^{\pi}$$

$$= 0.$$

Thus $\qquad\qquad \mathbf{f} \simeq 31.$

This time the Fourier Series is exact.

(iii) Combine Example 2 with part (ii) of this exercise to get

$$\mathbf{f} \simeq \left(\dfrac{\pi^2}{3}+1\right)\mathbf{1} - 4\left(\cos - \dfrac{\cos 2}{2^2} + \dfrac{\cos 3}{3^2} - \ldots\right).$$

(iv) Quite a number of applications of integration by parts are called for. Going straight to

Step 3 $\quad b_n = \dfrac{2}{\pi} \displaystyle\int_0^\pi (x^3 + x)\sin nx\,dx$

$$= \frac{2}{\pi}\left\{\left[(x^3+x).\frac{-\cos nx}{n}\right]_0^\pi + \frac{1}{n}\int_0^\pi (3x^2+1)\cos nx\,dx\right\}$$

$$= \frac{2}{\pi}\left\{\frac{(\pi^3+\pi)}{n}(-1)^{n+1} + \left[(3x^2+1)\frac{\sin nx}{n^2}\right]_0^\pi\right.$$

$$-\frac{1}{n^2}\int_0^\pi 6x\sin nx\,dx$$

$$= \frac{2}{\pi}\left\{\frac{(\pi^3+\pi)}{n}(-1)^{n+1} - \frac{6}{n^2}\left[x\frac{-\cos nx}{n}\right]_0^\pi\right.$$

$$\left. -\frac{6}{n^2}\int_0^\pi \cos nx\,dx\right\}$$

$$= 2\left(\frac{\pi^2+1}{n} - \frac{6}{n^2}\right)(-1)^{n+1}.$$

So that $\qquad \mathbf{f} \simeq \dots + 2\left(\dfrac{\pi^2+1}{n} - \dfrac{6}{n^2}\right)(-1)^{n+1}\sin n + \dots$

Notice that, buried in this formula, is the $x \to x$ term from Example 1 that we ought to expect to find.

2. (i) The formula gives

$$\frac{\pi}{2} = 2\left(\sin\left(\tfrac{1}{2}\pi\right) - \frac{\sin(\pi)}{2} + \frac{\sin\left(\tfrac{3}{2}\pi\right)}{3} - \frac{\sin(2\pi)}{4} + \frac{\sin\left(\tfrac{5}{2}\pi\right)}{5} - \dots\right).$$

Thus $\qquad\qquad \dfrac{\pi}{4} = 1 - \dfrac{1}{3} + \dfrac{1}{5} - \dfrac{1}{7} + \dots$

This formula is hopelessly inadequate for calculating π. We would need to calculate $\dfrac{\pi}{4}$ correct to 5 decimals. Errors in the calculation can arise from truncating the series after a finite number of terms and from rounding numbers to a specific number of decimal places. The truncation error in terminating the series after n terms is $\leqslant \dfrac{1}{2(n+1)}$, the next term in the series. To avoid an error in the 5th decimal place one could thus require $\dfrac{10^5}{2}$ terms, but the situation is even worse than this. Allowing for rounding errors we would have to calculate each term of the series correct to 10 decimal places. For if each term had an error of $0 \cdot 000\,000\,000\,1$ then after 10^5 terms we would accumulate a possible error of $0 \cdot 00001$ which could effect the accuracy of the estimation for π. So that a crude estimate of the number of terms needed would be $\frac{1}{2} \times 10^{10}$.

(ii) The formula gives

$$\frac{\pi^2}{4} \simeq \frac{\pi^2}{3} - 4\left(\cos(\tfrac{1}{2}\pi) - \frac{\cos(\pi)}{2^2} + \frac{\cos(\tfrac{3}{2}\pi)}{3^2} - \frac{\cos(2\pi)}{4^2} + \ldots\right).$$

Thus
$$\frac{\pi^2}{12} = 4\left(\frac{1}{2^2} - \frac{1}{4^2} + \frac{1}{6^2} - \frac{1}{8^2} + \ldots\right)$$

$$= 1 - \frac{1}{2^2} + \frac{1}{3^2} - \frac{1}{4^2} + \ldots.$$

Would you believe that 10^6 terms are needed? Although these series are clearly of no use for calculating π, that does not mean these results are useless. After all they certainly enable us to write down the sums of the series

$$1 - \frac{1}{3} + \frac{1}{5} - \frac{1}{7} + \ldots \quad \text{and} \quad 1 - \frac{1}{2^2} + \frac{1}{3^2} - \frac{1}{4^2} + \ldots.$$

3. $$O_f(x) = -\frac{f(-x) - f(-(-x))}{2} = -O_f(-x),$$

$$E_f(x) = \frac{f(-x) + f(-(-x))}{2} = E_f(-x),$$

$$O_f(x) + E_f(x) = \frac{f(x) - f(-x) + f(x) + f(-x)}{2} = f(x).$$

4. $b_n = 0$ because $f(x)\sin nx$ is odd.

$a_m = \dfrac{\pi}{2}\displaystyle\int_0^\pi f(x)\cos mx\,dx$ because $f(x)$ is even.

5. (i) $$f(x) \simeq \frac{\pi}{2} - \frac{4}{\pi}\left(\cos x + \frac{\cos 3x}{3^2} + \frac{\cos 5x}{5^2} + \ldots\right).$$

(ii) Integration by parts twice gives

$$a_m = \frac{2}{\pi}\left[\frac{e^x \sin mx}{m} + \frac{e^x \cos mx}{m^2}\right]_0^\pi - \frac{a_m}{m^2},$$

$$f(x) \simeq e^\pi - 1 + \frac{2}{\pi}\sum_{m=1}^{\infty}\frac{e^\pi(-1)^m - 1}{1 + m^2}\cos mx.$$

(iii) Writing $f(x) = \pi^2 - x^2$, we can use known results to give

$$f(x) \simeq \frac{2\pi^2}{3} + 4\left(\cos x - \frac{\cos 2x}{2^2} + \frac{\cos 3x}{3^2} - \ldots\right).$$

6. (i) See Example 1. (ii) See Exercise 5(i).

7. (i) (a) See Example 2.

$$(b) \; f(x) \simeq 2\pi\left(\sin x - \frac{\sin 2x}{2} + \frac{\sin 3x}{3} - \ldots\right)$$
$$- \frac{8}{\pi}\left(\sin x + \frac{\sin 3x}{3^2} + \frac{\sin 5x}{5^2} + \ldots\right).$$

(ii) Substitute $x = 0$ in the result of Exercise 6(ii).

8. (i) $$f(x) \simeq \frac{8}{\pi} \sum_{n=1}^{\infty} \frac{n}{4n^2 - 1} \sin 2nx.$$

(ii) $$f(x) \simeq \frac{2}{\pi} - \frac{4}{\pi} \sum_{n=1}^{\infty} \frac{\cos 2nx}{4n^2 - 1}.$$

Notice that this can be obtained from (i) by integration.

(iii) On the face of it, we seem to have expressed **cos** and **sin** as linear combinations of the other elements in the set, but these are not the 'proper' sine and cosine functions – they have restricted domains.

9. (i) $\int_{-L}^{L} f(x)g(x)\,\mathrm{d}x = \frac{L}{\pi}\int_{-\pi}^{\pi} f(u)f(g)\,\mathrm{d}u$, where $u = \dfrac{\pi x}{L}$,

and so the result follows from Theorem 2.1 on page 18.

(ii) As in (i).

10. Both results follow from the fact that if h has period $2L$,

$$\int_{a}^{a+2L} h(x)\,\mathrm{d}x = \int_{a}^{2L} h(x)\,\mathrm{d}x + \int_{2L}^{a+2L} h(x)\,\mathrm{d}x$$
$$= \int_{a}^{2L} h(x)\,\mathrm{d}x + \int_{0}^{a} h(u-2L)\,\mathrm{d}u$$
$$= \int_{a}^{2L} h(x)\,\mathrm{d}x + \int_{0}^{a} h(x)\,\mathrm{d}x.$$

11. The phenomena are essentially the same; for, although the function in Example 1 is continuous in $(-\pi, \pi)$, the Fourier series represents a function with domain R which is discontinued at $n\pi$ for all n.

Chapter 4

1.   (i) $\|\lambda\mathbf{a}\| = \sqrt[+]{(\lambda^2 a_1^2 + \lambda^2 a_2 + \lambda^2 a_3^2)}$
         $= |\lambda|\sqrt[+]{(a_1^2 + a_2^2 + a_3^2)}$
         $= |\lambda|\,\|\mathbf{a}\|.$

   (ii)   If $\|\mathbf{a}\| = 0,$ $a_1^2 + a_2^2 + a_3^2 = 0.$

So that each of the terms $a_i^2 = 0$ and $\mathbf{a} = \mathbf{0}$. Conversely, if $\mathbf{a} = \mathbf{0}$, the result $\|\mathbf{a}\| = 0$ is obvious.

2.   (i)   distance between $\mathbf{f}$ and $\mathbf{g}$
$$= [(\mathbf{f}-\mathbf{g}).(\mathbf{f}-\mathbf{g})]^{\frac{1}{2}}$$
$$= \left\{\int_a^b (f(x)-g(x))^2\mathrm{d}x\right\}^{\frac{1}{2}}.$$

   (ii) $\|\lambda\mathbf{f}\| = \left\{\int_a^b \lambda^2 f^2(x)\mathrm{d}x\right\}^{\frac{1}{2}}$
         $= |\lambda|\left\{\int_a^b f^2(x)\mathrm{d}x\right\}^{\frac{1}{2}}$
         $= |\lambda|\,\|\mathbf{f}\|.$

If $\|\mathbf{f}\| = 0$, then ... (see solution to Exercise 2. 2(i) and footnote).

   (iii) $\|\mathbf{f}-\mathbf{g}\| = \left\{\int_0^1 (x-x^2)^2\mathrm{d}x\right\}^{\frac{1}{2}}$
         $= \left\{\int_0^1 (x^2-2x^3+x^4)\mathrm{d}x\right\}^{\frac{1}{2}}$
         $= \{\tfrac{1}{3}-\tfrac{2}{4}+\tfrac{1}{5}\}^{\frac{1}{2}} = (\tfrac{1}{30})^{\frac{1}{2}}.$

   $\|\mathbf{f}-\mathbf{h}\| = \left\{\int_0^1 (x-x^3)^2\mathrm{d}x\right\}^{\frac{1}{2}}$
         $= \{\tfrac{1}{3}-\tfrac{2}{5}+\tfrac{1}{7}\}^{\frac{1}{2}} = (\tfrac{29}{105})^{\frac{1}{2}}.$

3.   (i) $\|\mathbf{f}\| = \left\{\int_0^1 x^2\mathrm{d}x\right\}^{\frac{1}{2}}$
         $= (\tfrac{1}{3})^{\frac{1}{2}}.$

So that the unit vector in the direction of $\mathbf{f}$ is
$$x \to \sqrt{3}\,x.$$
Similarly, the unit vectors in the direction of $\mathbf{g}$ and $\mathbf{h}$ are
$$x \to \sqrt{5}\,x^2 \quad \text{and} \quad x \to \sqrt{7}\,x^3$$
respectively.

(ii) $\dfrac{\mathbf{f}_i}{\|\mathbf{f}_i\|}\cdot\dfrac{\mathbf{f}_j}{\|\mathbf{f}_j\|} = \displaystyle\int_a^b \dfrac{f_i(x)}{\|\mathbf{f}_i\|}\cdot\dfrac{f_j(x)}{\|\mathbf{f}_j\|}\,\mathrm{d}x$

$$= \frac{1}{\|\mathbf{f}_i\|\,\|\mathbf{f}_j\|}\int_a^b f_i(x)f_j(x)\,\mathrm{d}x$$

$$= \begin{cases} 0 \text{ if } i \neq j \text{ since the } \mathbf{f}_i\text{'s are orthogonal,} \\ 1 \text{ if } i = j \text{ since } \displaystyle\int_a^b f_i^2(x)\,\mathrm{d}x = \|\mathbf{f}_i\|^2. \end{cases}$$

4. Consider the sequence of partial sums

$$S_n = \sum_{i=1}^{n} s_i.$$

Since each s_i is positive, we know that

$$S_1 \leqslant S_2 \leqslant \ldots \leqslant S_n \leqslant \ldots \leqslant K$$

so that K is an upper bound of $\{S_n\}$. Without proving it, we will use the result that every set of real numbers which is bounded above has a least upper bound; let us denote the least upper bound of $\{S_n\}$ by K_1. Then, to show that

$$\lim_{n \to \infty} s_i = 0,$$

we need to prove that, given $\epsilon > 0$, $\exists N$ such that

$$n > N \Rightarrow |s_n| < \epsilon.$$

Now, given $\epsilon > 0$, $\exists N$ such that

$$K_1 - \epsilon < S_N \leqslant K_1$$

by the definition of least upper bound and further

$$S_N \leqslant S_{n-1} \leqslant S_n \leqslant K_1$$

if $n > N$. So that, if $n > N$,

$$S_n - S_{n-1} < K_1 - (K_1 - \epsilon)$$

$$\therefore \quad 0 < s_n < \epsilon$$

since we know that each s_i is positive.

$$\therefore \quad n > N \Rightarrow |s_n| < \epsilon.$$

5. (i) This is a direct consequence of the result on page 52, obtained by using the theorem that one can rearrange the terms of a convergent positive sequence without affecting the convergence.

(ii) The sequence of partial sums

$$\sum_{i=1}^{n} (a_i^2 + b_i^2)$$

is bounded above by **f.f**. So, using the argument of Exercise 4,

$$\lim_{i \to \infty} (a_i^2 + b_i^2) = 0.$$

Thus given $\epsilon > 0$, $\exists N$ such that for all $n > N$

$$0 \leqslant a_n^2 + b_n^2 < \epsilon^2,$$

$$\therefore \quad 0 \leqslant a_n^2 < \epsilon^2 \text{ since } b_n^2 \geqslant 0,$$

$$\therefore \quad |a_n| < \epsilon.$$

So that
$$\lim_{i \to \infty} a_i = 0.$$

Similarly we can show that $\lim_{i \to \infty} b_i = 0$.

6. $\quad \|\mathbf{f}_k - \mathbf{1}\|^2 = \displaystyle\int_0^1 (x^{\frac{1}{k}} - 1)^2 \mathrm{d}x$

$$= \int_0^1 (x^{\frac{2}{k}} - 2x^{\frac{1}{k}} + 1)\,\mathrm{d}x$$

$$= \left[\frac{1}{1 + \dfrac{2}{k}} x^{1 + \frac{2}{k}} - \frac{2}{1 + \dfrac{1}{k}} x^{1 + \frac{1}{k}} + x \right]_0^1$$

$$= \frac{1}{1 + \dfrac{2}{k}} - \frac{2}{1 + \dfrac{1}{k}} + 1.$$

So that
$$\lim_{k \to \infty} \|\mathbf{f}_k - \mathbf{1}\| = 0.$$

The sequence $\{\mathbf{f}_k\}$ *is* point-wise convergent in the interval $[0, 1]$, but not to the function $x \to 1$, rather, to the function

$$x \to \begin{cases} 0 & x = 0 \\ 1 & \text{otherwise} \end{cases} \quad (x \in [0, 1]),$$

so we have an example of a sequence of functions, each continuous, whose point-wise limit is not a continuous function.

7. The argument is almost exactly the same as the one given for (1). All that changes is the observation that

$$\frac{\delta}{2} < \frac{x - a}{2} \leqslant \pi$$

in the interval $[a+\delta, \pi]$ so that $\cot\left(\dfrac{x-a}{2}\right)$ is still bounded and continuous.

8. Replace $f(a_-)$ by $f(a_+)$ and $\epsilon(x)$ by $y\eta(x)$ in the argument given for $(2a)$ and the same argument applies.

Chapter 6

1. $\displaystyle\int_{-1}^{1} D^n(x^2-1)^n\, D^m(x^2-1)^m\, dx$

$$= [D^{n-1}(x^2-1)^n\, D^m(x^2-1)^m]_{-1}^1$$
$$-\int_{-1}^{1} D^{n-1}(x^2-1)^n\, D^{m+1}(x^2-1)^m\, dx$$
$$= -\int_{-1}^{1} D^{n-1}(x^2-1)\, D^{m+1}(x^2-1)^m\, dx.$$

Suppose $m < n$, then repeating this process another $m-1$ times gives

$$\int_{-1}^{1} D^{n-m}(x^2-1)^n\, D^{2m}(x^2-1)^m\, dx$$
$$= (2m)!\int_{-1}^{1} D^{n-m}(x^2-1)^n\, dx$$
$$= 0.$$

Since differentiating $(x^2-1)^n$ only $n-m$ times will give $(x^2-1)^m$ $\times$ {polynomial} and this expression is zero at 1 and -1.

2. The first thing to worry about is why the H_m's are called Hermite *polynomials* with all the exponential terms cluttering up the place. When $e^{-\frac{x^2}{2}}$ is differentiated any number of times, $e^{-\frac{x^2}{2}}$ will appear in every term, and when this is factored out one will be left with a polynomial. Thus $e^{\frac{x^2}{2}} D^m(e^{-\frac{x^2}{2}})$ is indeed a polynomial. Now, for orthogonality we need to look at

$$\mathbf{H_m}\cdot\mathbf{H_n} = \int_{-\infty}^{\infty} e^{-\frac{x^2}{2}} H_m(x)(-1)^n e^{\frac{x^2}{2}} D^n(e^{-\frac{x^2}{2}})\, dx$$

where, say, $m < n$. Integration by parts gives

$$(-1)^n[H_m(x)D^{n-1}(e^{-\frac{x^2}{2}})]_{-\infty}^{\infty} - \int_{-\infty}^{\infty} H_m'(x)D^{n-1}(e^{-\frac{x^2}{2}})\, dx.$$

The first term vanishes, because it involves the product of a polynomial and $e^{-\frac{x^2}{2}}$, and so vanishes as x approaches $\pm \infty$. Repeating the procedure another $m-1$ times gives

$$(-1)^{m+n} \int_{-\infty}^{\infty} H_m^{(m)}(x) D^{n-m}(e^{-\frac{x^2}{2}}) dx.$$

But $H_m^{(m)}(x) = m!$, proved at the end of the solution, and so we get

$$(-1)^{m+n} m! \int_{-\infty}^{\infty} D^{n-m}(e^{-\frac{x^2}{2}}) dx$$

$$= (-1)^{m+n} m! \, [D^{n-m-1}(e^{-\frac{x^2}{2}})]_{-\infty}^{\infty}$$

$$= 0,$$

since the term in brackets is the product of a polynomial and $e^{-\frac{x^2}{2}}$. Probably the best way to show that $H_m^{(m)}(x) = m!$ is to note that $H_m(x)$ is a polynomial of degree m and leading coefficient 1. It is easy to see that $H_0(x) = 1$, so we try induction. First of all we have

$$(-1)^m e^{-\frac{x^2}{2}} H_m(x) = D^m(e^{-\frac{x^2}{2}}),$$

and so $\quad D^{m+1}(e^{-\frac{x^2}{2}}) = (-1)^m \{-x H_m(x) + H_m'(x)\} e^{-\frac{x^2}{2}}.$

But $\qquad\qquad D^{m+1} e^{-\frac{x^2}{2}} = (-1)^{m+1} e^{-\frac{x^2}{2}} H_{m+1}(x),$

and so $\qquad\qquad H_{m+1}(x) = x H_m(x) - H_m'(x).$

If $H_m(x)$ is a polynomial of degree m with leading coefficient 1, then it follows that $H_{m+1}(x)$ is also. Thus, since $H_0(x) = 1$, the required result is proved by induction. The fact that $H_m^{(m)}(x) = m!$ now follows because $D^m x^m = m!$.

3. (i) $p(x) = 1 - x^2$, $q(x) = 0$, $r(x) = 1$, $\lambda = n(n+1)$.

Substitution into the equation shows that $P_n(x)$ is a solution corresponding to $\lambda = n(n+1)$. Further, since $p(x)$ vanishes at $x = \pm 1$, the differential operator is symmetric. Hence the eigenfunctions $P_n(x)$, are orthogonal.

(ii) $p(x) = e^{-\frac{x^2}{2}}$, $q(x) = 0$, $r(x) = e^{-\frac{x^2}{2}}$, $\lambda = n$.

The equation obtained is actually $e^{-\frac{x^2}{2}}$ times the original equation –

one can regard the two equations as equivalent. Although we have considered symmetric operators only on finite intervals, one can get an idea as to what might happen in the interval $(-\infty, \infty)$. Any space of functions for which

$$e^{-\frac{x^2}{2}}(Df(x))g(x) \to 0 \quad \text{as} \quad x \to \pm\infty$$

will be a suitable domain to make the operator symmetric. We know that this is the case for the solutions of this equation (which are polynomials), and so the eigenfunctions (the Hermite polynomials) are orthogonal with respect to the inner product

$$\mathbf{f.g} = \int_{-\infty}^{\infty} e^{-\frac{x^2}{2}} f(x)g(x)\,\mathrm{d}x.$$

4.   Any boundary conditions of the form

$$A_1 f(0) + A_2 f'(0) = 0,$$

$$B_1 f(l) + B_2 f'(l) = 0,$$

where A_1, A_2, B_1 and B_2 are constants, will make the operator symmetric.

Miscellaneous Exercises

1.   What are the periods of the following functions, all with domain R?

(i) $x \to \cos\dfrac{2\pi x}{7}$;

(ii) $x \to \sin\dfrac{\pi x}{8}$;

(iii) $x \to 2\sin\dfrac{\pi x}{8}$;

(iv) $x \to \cos\dfrac{2\pi x}{7} + \sin\dfrac{\pi x}{7}$;

(v) $x \to 1 + \sin 3x$;

(vi) $x \to (\sin 3x)(\cos 4x)$.

9   GFS

125

2. Two functions, **f** and **g**, have periods a and b respectively $(a, b \in Z)$. Are the functions **f**+**g** and **f**×**g** necessarily periodic? If so, what are their periods?

3. What is the minimum value of n, if the polynomial

$$\mathbf{f}: x \to a_0 + a_1 x + a_2 x^2 + \ldots + a_n x^n$$

is to have specified images at k points in its domain?

4. A function **f** with domain R is such that

$$f(x + \pi) = -f(x)$$

for all $x \in$ R. Prove that **f** is periodic with period 2π. If this function is to be represented as a series in the form

$$f(x) = a_0 + a_1 \cos x + a_2 \cos 2x + \ldots$$
$$+ b_1 \sin x + b_2 \sin 2x + \ldots$$

what can you deduce about the coefficients a_0, a_1, ... and b_1, b_2, ...?

5. Let **f** be a periodic function with domain R and period 2π, and let $a \in$ R, $b \in$ R. Show that

$$\int_a^b f(x)\,dx = \int_{a+2\pi}^{b+2\pi} f(x)\,dx = \int_{a-2\pi}^{b-2\pi} f(x)\,dx.$$

Show, also that

$$\int_{-\pi}^{\pi} f(x+a)\,dx = \int_{-\pi}^{\pi} f(x)\,dx = \int_{-\pi+a}^{\pi+a} f(x)\,dx.$$

6. A function **f** with domain R is periodic with period 2 and

$$\mathbf{f}: x \to |x| \quad (|x| \leqslant 1).$$

It is intended to represent f in the form

$$f(x) = a_0 + a_1 \cos kx + a_2 \cos 2kx + \ldots.$$

What is the value of k? What can you say about $\sum_{i=0}^{\infty} a_i$?

7. For the scalar product defined by

$$\mathbf{f} . \mathbf{g} = \int_0^1 f(x)g(x)\,dx$$

on a suitable space of functions, which of the following pairs of functions are orthogonal? (All functions have domain R.)

(i) $\qquad x \to x,\ x \to x^2$;

(ii) $\qquad x \to x,\ x \to 1 - \dfrac{3x}{2}$;

(iii) $\qquad x \to e^x,\ x \to (e^2 - 1)e^{-x} - 2e^x$;

(iv) $\qquad x \to e^x,\ x \to e^{-x}$.

8. Referring to Exercise 3 of Chapter 2, how would you define such a thing as the 'angle' between two vectors in terms of a scalar product? Using the scalar product in Exericse 7 above, calculate the 'angle' between the following pairs of functions.

(i) $\qquad x \to x,\ x \to x^3$;

(ii) $\qquad x \to x,\ x \to 2x$;

(iii) $\qquad x \to \sin x,\ x \to \cos x$.

9. Show that the set

$$\{\sin,\ \sin 2,\ \sin 3,\ \sin 4,\ \ldots\}$$

does not form a basis for the space $\mathscr{F}$ on page 15 of Chapter 2.

10. Prove that any subset of a linearly independent set is linearly independent.

11. Test each of the following potential scalar products for the properties in Exercise 2 of Chapter 2.

(*a*) For the set of three-dimensional geometric vectors, with $\mathbf{x} = x_1\mathbf{i} + x_2\mathbf{j} + x_3\mathbf{k}$ and $\mathbf{y} = y_i\mathbf{i} + y_2\mathbf{j} + y_3\mathbf{k}$, define $\mathbf{x}.\mathbf{y}$ as

(1) $x_1y_1 + x_2y_2 + 3x_3y_3$,

(2) $x_1y_1 + x_2y_2 + x_3y_3 + 2x_1y_2$,

(3) $x_1^2 + y_1^2$,

(4) $x_1y_1 + x_2y_2 + x_3y_3 - \frac{1}{2}x_2y_3 - \frac{1}{2}x_3y_2$.

(*b*) $\mathbf{A}$ and $\mathbf{B}$ are $n \times n$ matrices of real numbers and $\mathbf{A}.\mathbf{B} =$ the sum of the diagonal elements of $\mathbf{A} \times \mathbf{B}$.

(*c*) For a suitable space of functions, define **f.g** as

(1) $\mathbf{f.g} = \int_{-1}^{1} xf(x)g(x)\mathrm{d}x,$

(2) $\mathbf{f.g} = \int_{0}^{\infty} \mathrm{e}^{-x}f(x)g(x)\mathrm{d}x,$

(3) $\mathbf{f.g} = \int_{-1}^{1} x^2f(x)g(x)\mathrm{d}x.$

12. Show that $(\mathbf{x.y})^2 = (\mathbf{x.x}).(\mathbf{y.y})$ if and only if $\mathbf{x}$, $\mathbf{y}$ are linearly dependent.

13. In Exercise 4 of Chapter 2 we obtained the inequality

$$(\mathbf{u.v})^2 \leqslant (\mathbf{u.u})\,(\mathbf{v.v}).$$

Assuming a suitable space of functions, and taking appropriate values of *a* and *b* in the scalar product.

$$\mathbf{f.g} = \int_{a}^{b} f(x)g(x)\mathrm{d}x$$

show that

(i) $\int_{0}^{\pi} \sqrt{[(x\cos x)]}\mathrm{d}x \leqslant \pi;$

(ii) $\int_{0}^{\frac{1}{2}} \frac{1}{\sqrt{(1-x)}}\,\mathrm{d}x \leqslant \sqrt{(\frac{1}{2}\ln(2))}.$

14. If **f** is any odd function with domain R, and **g** is any even function with domain R, show that **f** and **g** are orthogonal with respect to the scalar product

$$\mathbf{f.g} = \int_{-a}^{a} f(x)g(x)\mathrm{d}x,$$

where *a* is any real number.

15. Consider the list

$$\mathbf{x} = (x_1, x_2, x_3, ..., x_n),$$

where $x_i \in$ R. This set forms a vector space. Verify that the mapping

$$(\mathbf{x}, \mathbf{y}) \to \mathbf{x.y} = \sum_{i=1}^{n} x_i y_i,$$

(where $\mathbf{y} = (y_1, y_2, y_3, ..., y_n)$) satisfies the properties in Exercise 3 of Chapter 2. Show that the following set of vectors is orthogonal (in the sense that $e_i.e_j = 0$).

$$\mathbf{e}_1 = (1, 0, 0, ..., 0),$$

$$\mathbf{e}_2 = (0, 1, 0, ..., 0),$$

$$\mathbf{e}_3 = (0, 0, 1, ..., 0),$$

$$\dotfill$$

$$\mathbf{e}_n = (0, 0, 0, ..., 1).$$

16.   Consider a list of n pairs of measurements from an experiment:

$$(x_1, y_1), (x_2, y_2), ..., (x_n, y_n).$$

These measurements can be represented by two vectors

$$\mathbf{x} = (x_1, y_2, ..., x_n),$$

$$\mathbf{y} = (y_1, y_2, ..., y_n)$$

in the space introduced in Exercise 15. Writing $\bar{x}$ and $\bar{y}$ as the means of the x and y measurements respectively, we can define two new vectors

$$\mathbf{d}_x = (x_1-\bar{x}, x_2-\bar{x}, ..., x_n-\bar{x}),$$

$$\mathbf{d}_y = (y_1-\bar{y}, y_2-\bar{y}, ..., y_n-\bar{y}).$$

(i)   Show that with the scalar product of Exercise 15,

$\dfrac{1}{n}(\mathbf{d_x}.\mathbf{d_x}) = \sigma_x$, the standard deviation of the x measurements,

$\dfrac{1}{n}(\mathbf{d_y}.\mathbf{d_y}) = \sigma_y$, the standard deviation of the y measurements.

(ii)   Writing $\dfrac{1}{n}(\mathbf{d_x}.\mathbf{d_y}) = \sigma_{xy}$, use the inequality of Exercise 3 of Chapter 2 to show that $\left| \dfrac{\sigma_{xy}}{\sigma_x \sigma_y} \right| \leqslant 1.$

(iii)   Show that $\left| \dfrac{\sigma_{xy}}{\sigma_x \sigma_y} \right| = 1$, if and only if $\mathbf{x}$ is linearly dependent on $\mathbf{y}$. Interpret this in terms of the original data.

17. With respect to the inner product

$$\mathbf{f}.\mathbf{g} = \int_a^b f(x)g(x)\mathrm{d}x$$

can numbers a and b be found to make the functions $x \to x$, $x \to x^2$, $x \to x^3$ orthogonal?

18. Find the 'distance' between the functions

$$x \to x^2 \quad (x \in [-1, 1]),$$

$$x \to x \quad (x \in [-1, 1]),$$

with respect to each of the inner products

(i) $\mathbf{f}.\mathbf{g} = \displaystyle\int_{-1}^{1} f(x)g(x)\mathrm{d}x$

(ii) $\mathbf{f}.\mathbf{g} = \displaystyle\int_{-1}^{1} |f(x)-g(x)|\,\mathrm{d}x.$

19. Find the Fourier Series for $\mathbf{f}$, where

$$f(x) = \frac{\pi - x}{2} \quad (x \in [0, 2\pi]).$$

Sketch the graph of the Fourier Series for $x \in [-2\pi, 4\pi]$.

20. Find the Fourier Series for $\mathbf{f}$, where

$$f(x) = e^x \quad (x \in [-\pi, \pi]).$$

21. Find the Fourier Series for $\mathbf{f}$, where

(i) $f(x) = |\cos x| \quad (x \in [-\pi, \pi])$,

(ii) $f(x) = |\sin x| \quad (x \in [-\pi, \pi])$.

22. Find the Fourier cosine series for $\mathbf{f}$, where

$$f(x) = \pi - x \quad (x \in [0, \pi]).$$

23. Find the Fourier sine series for $\mathbf{f}$, where

$$f(x) = \pi - x \quad (x \in [0, \pi]).$$

24. (i) Find the Fourier series for $\mathbf{f}$, where

$$f(x) = \cos \mu x \quad (x \in (-\pi, \pi)),$$

where μ is not an integer.

(ii) By substituting $x = \pi$ into your result for (i), deduce that

$$\cot \mu\pi = \frac{2\mu}{\pi}\left(\frac{1}{2\mu^2} + \frac{1}{\mu^2 - 1} + \frac{1}{\mu^2 - 2^2} + \dots\right).$$

(iii) Assuming that all necessary integrations can be justified, integrate the expressions in (ii) between limits 0 and x to obtain

$$\ln\left(\frac{\sin \pi x}{\pi x}\right) = \ln\left(1 - \frac{x^2}{1^2}\right) + \ln\left(1 - \frac{x^2}{2^2}\right) + \dots,$$

and hence that

$$\sin \pi x = \pi x\left(1 - \frac{x^2}{1^2}\right)\left(1 - \frac{x^2}{2^2}\right)\left(1 - \frac{x^2}{3^2}\right)\dots.$$

(iv) Obtain the formula

$$\frac{\pi}{2} = \frac{2}{1} \cdot \frac{2}{3} \cdot \frac{4}{3} \cdot \frac{4}{5} \dots.$$

25. Use the results

$$\sum_{r=1}^{n-1} \sin\left(\frac{rp\pi}{n}\right)\sin\left(\frac{rq\pi}{n}\right) = 0 \quad (p, q < n, p \neq q),$$

$$\sum_{r=1}^{n-1} \left(\sin\frac{rp\pi}{n}\right)^2 = \frac{n}{2} \quad (p < n)$$

to find coefficients $b_1, b_2, \dots, b_{n-1}$, such that the curve with equation

$$y = b_1\sin\frac{\pi x}{L} + b_2\sin\frac{2\pi x}{L} + b_3\sin\frac{3\pi x}{L} + \dots + b_{n-1}\sin\frac{(n-1)\pi x}{L}$$

passes through the points

$$\left(\frac{L}{n}, y_1\right), \left(\frac{2L}{n}, y_2\right), \left(\frac{3L}{n}, y_3\right), \dots, \left(\frac{(n-1)L}{n}, y_{n-1}\right),$$

(Compare this problem with the text on page 6. Compare your answer with the formula for Fourier coefficients.)

26. (i) A continuous function **f** with domain R is periodic with period 2π and has Fourier coefficients a_k and b_k. Show that the function **F**, where

$$F(x) = \int_0^x \left[f(t) - \frac{a_0}{2}\right] dt$$

is periodic with period 2π.

(ii) The function **F** in (i) is also continuous and has a piece-wise continuous first derivative (prove this if you feel good). Calculate the Fourier coefficients, A_k, B_k of **F**.

(iii) Deduce that $\int_a^b f(x)\,\mathrm{d}x$ can be evaluated by integrating the Fourier series of **f** term by term.

27. Let **f** be a continuous function with domain R and period 2π, with a piece-wise continuous first derivative **f'**. Prove that the Fourier Series for **f'** can be obtained by differentiating the series for **f** term by term, and that this series converges to $f'(x)$ whenever $f'(x)$ exists.

28. (*a*) An experiment is performed and produces the following set of data

$$(x_1, y_1), (x_2, y_2), ..., (x_n, y_n).$$

It is required to find the line through the origin which 'best fits' these data. The usual approach to this problem is to draw the line with equation $y = kx$ so that the sum of the squares of the values $(kx_i - y_i)$ is as small as possible. This is the 'method of least squares', and the problem is to calculate k. Clearly, actually drawing the line is not very satisfactory.

(i) Writing $\mathbf{x} = (x_1, x_2, ..., x_n)$ and $\mathbf{y} = (y_1, y_2, ..., y_n)$, express this problem in terms of norms.

(ii) From (i) we see that the problem can be considered to be that of find k so that $k\mathbf{x}$ is the best approximation in the least squares sense to $\mathbf{y}$, so that k is the 'Fourier coefficient' of $\mathbf{y}$ with respect to the single vector $\mathbf{x}$. Calculate k, using the inner product of Exercise 15.

(*b*) Find k so that the line $y = kx$ best fits each of the following sets of points in the 'least squares' sense:

(i) (4, 3), (6, 7), (8, 10),

(ii) (2, 1), (6, 4), (10, 6), (14, 6).

29. The transverse vibrations of a beam of length l freely hinged at each end satisfy the equation

$$kD_x^4 u + D_t^2 u = 0,$$

where $u(x, t)$ is the displacement of the beam at time t at a point distance x along the beam from one end. The constant k depends on the physical characteristics of the beam. Show that the substitution

$u(x, t) = y(x) e^{i\omega t}$ with $D^2 y = 0$ and $y = 0$ at $x = 0$ and $x = l$ produces the equation

$$D_y^4 - \frac{\omega^2}{k} y = 0.$$

Show that the vibrations which correspond to the eigenfunctions of this system have frequencies $\dfrac{n^2 \pi \sqrt{k}}{2l^2}$.

30. The steady temperature $u(r, \theta)$ at the point with polar co-ordinates (r, θ) on a flat plate satisfies Laplace's equation:

$$D_r^2 u + \frac{1}{r} D_r u + \frac{1}{r^2} D_\theta^2 u = 0.$$

If the temperature on a circle centre the origin radius a is to satisfy

$$u(a, \theta) = f(\theta),$$

where f is some given function find an expression for $u(r, \theta)$ throughout the interior of this circle. (Try separating the variables using $Ru(r, \theta) = (r) \Theta(\theta)$. Find the eigenvalues. The equation in R may be simplified using the substitution $R(r) = r^\alpha$, where α is to be found. To find the eigenvalues, use the fact that the solution must be unique at any given point and that a point (r, θ) is also described by $(r, \theta + 2n\pi)$, n an integer.)

31. Show that in the space of (continuous, four times differentiable) functions with domain $[-1, 1]$ satisfying the conditions

$$y(0) = y(1) = 0,$$

$$y''(0) = y''(1) = 0,$$

the operator L, where $Ly = -D^4 y$, is symmetric. Show that the eigenvalues satisfy

$$\sin(\lambda^{\frac{1}{4}}) \sinh(\lambda^{\frac{1}{4}}) = 0,$$

and write down the solution to the equation $Ly = \lambda y$ corresponding to the eigenvalue λ_n.

(This boundary value problem is important in the study of rotating shafts.)

Answers to Miscellaneous Exercises

1. (i) 7; (ii) 16; (iii) 16; (iv) 14; (v) $\dfrac{2\pi}{3}$; (vi) 2π.

2. $\mathbf{f}+\mathbf{g}$ and $\mathbf{f}\times\mathbf{g}$ are both periodic with period equal to the least common multiple of a and b.

3. $n = k-1$. If $n > k-1$ then more than one curve can fit the k points.

4. $\begin{aligned}
b_k &= \int_{-\pi}^{\pi} f(x)\sin kx\,dx = \int_{-\pi}^{0} f(x)\sin kx\,dx + \int_{0}^{\pi} f(x)\sin kx\,dx \\[2mm]
&= \int_{-\pi}^{0} f(x)\sin kx\,dx \\[2mm]
&\quad + \int_{-\pi}^{0} f(x+\pi)\sin(kx+k\pi)\,dx \\[2mm]
&= \int_{-\pi}^{0} f(x)\sin kx\,dx \\[2mm]
&\quad - \int_{-\pi}^{\pi} f(x+\pi)\sin(kx+k\pi)\,dx \\[2mm]
&= 0, \quad \text{if } k \text{ is even.}
\end{aligned}$

Thus, the even b_k's are zero. Similarly, the even a_k's are zero.

6. $k = \pi$, $\sum\limits_{i=0}^{\infty} a_i = 0$ (if the series is to converge to $f(0)$ when $x = 0$).

7. (ii), (iii).

8. Using $\cos\theta = \dfrac{\mathbf{x}\cdot\mathbf{y}}{\{(\mathbf{x}\cdot\mathbf{x})(\mathbf{y}\cdot\mathbf{y})\}^{\frac{1}{2}}}$, we get

(i) $\cos\theta = \dfrac{21}{5}$;

(ii) $\cos\theta = 1$; i.e. $\theta = 0$ corresponding to the fact that the two vectors are linearly dependent.

(iii) $\cos\theta = \dfrac{2\sin^2 1}{\left(1-\dfrac{\sin^2 2}{4}\right)^{\frac{1}{2}}}$.

11. (a) (1) has properties (i), (ii), (iii).

(2) (iii) only.

(3) (ii) only.

(4) (i), (ii), (iii).

(b) (ii), (iii).

(c) (1) (ii), (iii) (Property (i) would also hold if the limits of integration were 0 and 1).

(2) (i), (ii), (iii) (Provided the integrals exist, which is what is meant by a 'suitable' space of functions).

(3) (i), (ii), (iii).

18. (i) 0; (ii) $\frac{1}{3}$.

19. $\left\{\dfrac{\sin x}{1}+\dfrac{\sin 2x}{2}+\dfrac{\sin 3x}{3}+...\right\}.$

20. $\dfrac{e^{\pi}-e^{-\pi}}{\pi}\left\{\dfrac{1}{2}-\dfrac{1}{1+1^2}(\cos x-\sin x)+\dfrac{1}{1+2^2}(\cos 2x-\sin 2x)...\right\}.$

21. (i) $1-\dfrac{2}{\pi}\displaystyle\sum_{n=1}^{\infty}\dfrac{(-1)^n\cos 2nx}{4n^2-1};$

(ii) $\dfrac{2}{\pi}-\dfrac{4}{\pi}\displaystyle\sum_{n=1}^{\infty}\dfrac{\cos 2nx}{4n^2-1}.$

22. $\dfrac{\pi}{2}-\dfrac{4}{\pi}\displaystyle\sum_{n=0}^{\infty}\dfrac{\cos(2n+1)x}{(2n+1)^2}.$

23. $4\left[\sin x+\dfrac{\sin 3x}{3}+\dfrac{\sin 5x}{5}+...\right]-2\left[\sin x-\dfrac{\sin 2x}{2}+\dfrac{\sin 3x}{3}-...\right].$

(Notice that this can be obtained from the sine series for $f(x) = \pi$, $x \in [0, \pi]$ and $f(x) = x$, $x \in [-\pi, \pi]$ derived in the text.)

24. $\cos\mu x = \dfrac{2\mu\sin\mu\pi}{\pi}\left[\dfrac{1}{2\mu^2}-\dfrac{\cos x}{\mu^2-1}+\dfrac{\mu^2-2^2}{\cos 2x}-...+...\right]$

$(x \in (-\pi, \pi)).$

25. $b_r = \dfrac{2}{n}\displaystyle\sum_{j=1}^{n}y_j\sin\dfrac{rj\pi}{n}.$

As n gets larger and larger, this summation approaches more and more closely to an integral of the form we have used for Fourier coefficients.

28. (a) (i) $\qquad \|k\mathbf{x}-\mathbf{y}\|^2 = (k\mathbf{x}-\mathbf{y}).(k\mathbf{x}-\mathbf{y})$

$$= \sum_{i-1}^{\infty} (kx_i - y_i)^2.$$

Thus the problems is that of choosing k to make $\|k\mathbf{x}-\mathbf{y}\|$ as small as possible, i.e. to make $k\mathbf{x}$ as 'close' to $\mathbf{y}$ as possible.

(ii) $\qquad k = \dfrac{\mathbf{x}.\mathbf{y}}{\mathbf{x}.\mathbf{x}} = \dfrac{x_1 y_1 + x_2 y_2 + \ldots + x_k y_k}{x_1^2 + x_2^2 + \ldots + x_n^2}.$

(b) (i) $\qquad k = \frac{134}{116};$

(ii) $\qquad k = \frac{190}{336}.$

30. $u(r, \theta) = R(r)\,\Theta(\theta)$ gives

$$D^2\Theta(\theta) + \lambda\Theta(\theta) = 0,$$

$$r^2 D^2 R(r) + r D R(r) = \lambda R(r).$$

Thus $\qquad \Theta(\theta) = A\cos\sqrt{\lambda}\,\theta + B\sin\sqrt{\lambda}\,\theta.$

For uniqueness at any given point $\cos\sqrt{\lambda}\,(\theta + k2\pi)$ and $\sin\sqrt{\lambda}\,(\theta + k2\pi)$ (k an integer) must give $\cos\sqrt{\lambda}\,\theta$ and $\sin\sqrt{\lambda}\,\theta$ respectively. Thus $\lambda = n^2$, n any integer. This gives a sample solution

$$\Theta_n(\theta) = A_n\cos n\theta + B_n\sin n\theta.$$

The equation for R gives

$$R_n(r) = C_n r^n + D_n r^{-n}.$$

for a solution to exist at $r = 0$, $D_n = 0$. Thus

$$u(r, \theta) = \sum_{n=1}^{\infty} r^n(E_n\cos n\theta + F_n\sin n\theta).$$

Using the condition at $r = a$, $a^n E_n$ and $a^n F_n$ are the Fourier coefficients of f.

31. To complete the first part, notice that, for the equations

$$B\sinh(\lambda^{\frac{1}{4}}) + D\sin(\lambda^{\frac{1}{4}}) = 0,$$

$$B\sinh(\lambda^{\frac{1}{4}}) - D\sin(\lambda^{\frac{1}{4}}) = 0,$$

to have non-trivial solutions in B and D, the coefficients of B and D in the equations must be proportional. The solution is

$$y(x) = B\sinh(\lambda_n^{\frac{1}{4}} x) + D\sin(\lambda_n^{\frac{1}{4}} x).$$

Bibliography

The first two books in this list are referred to in our text for specific purposes. The book by Lanczos gives a fuller description of the conditions under which Fourier Series can be used safely; the Open University course discusses a number of aspects relevant to the material and approach in this text.

E. C. Titchmarsh, *The Theory of Functions.* (Oxford).

E. Whittaker and G. N. Watson, *A Course of Modern Analysis.* (Cambridge).

C. Lanczos, *Fourier Series.* (Oliver and Boyd).

Linear Mathematics. (The Open University Press).

Index